FOURTH EDITION

Green Building Guidelines

Meeting the Demand for Low-Energy, Resource-Efficient Homes

U.S. Department of Energy

The U.S. Department of Energy's Building America Program is reengineering the American home for energy efficiency and affordability. Building America works with the residential building industry to develop and implement innovative building processes and technologies—innovations that save builders and homeowners millions of dollars in construction and energy costs. This industry-led, cost-shared partnership program uses a systems engineering approach to reduce construction time and waste, as well as increase energy efficiency and use of renewable energy.

The research conducted by Building America teams improves the quality and performance of today's home and provides valuable information for homes of the future. By supporting the development of innovative home designs, building methods, and technologies that achieve significant energy and cost savings, the Building America Program is helping to shape the future of American homes.

Visit our Web site at www.buildingamerica.gov for more information.

Want more information?

To purchase additional copies of the *Green Building Guidelines,* visit BuilderBooks.com or the SBIC Web site at www.SBICouncil.org. To arrange for a *Green Building Guidelines* seminar tailored to your community, contact the Sustainable Buildings Industry Council at (202) 628-7400 ext. 210.

Disclaimer

Special thanks to

North American Insulation
Manufacturers Association

ECO-BLOCK

THE BEST FORM FOR
ANY FUNCTION

for sponsoring the printing
of this version of

Green Building Guidelines:
Meeting the Demand for Low-Energy, Resource-Efficient Homes

For more information:

NAIMA
44 Canal Center Plaza
Suite 310
Alexandria, VA 22314
Phone: (703) 684-0084
Fax: (703) 684-0427
Web: www.naima.org

BASF
3000 Continental Drive -
North (MS 4-015)
Mt. Olive, NJ 07828
Phone: (973) 426-4838
Fax: (973) 426-3904
Web: www.basf.com

ECO-Block LLC
11200 Grader Street
Suite 700
Dallas, TX 75238
Phone: (214) 503-1644
Fax: (214) 342-5322
Web: www.eco-block.com

FOURTH EDITION

Green Building Guidelines

Meeting the Demand for Low-Energy, Resource-Efficient Homes

Acknowledgments

Content for the *Green Building Guidelines* was derived from numerous existing resources, primarily *Passive Solar Design Strategies: Guidelines for Home Building,* developed by the members of the Sustainable Buildings Industry Council (formerly known as the Passive Solar Industries Council). Extensive information and graphics were pulled from the NAHB Research Center's *A Guide to Developing Green Builder Programs* and Georgia Environmental Facilities Authority's *A Builder's Guide to Energy Efficient Homes in Georgia.* Content was also extracted from many publicly funded Web sites (U.S. Department of Energy, California Energy Commission, etc.) and the following publications:

Designing Low-Energy Buildings with Energy-10, SBIC
E Seal Certification Manual, Edison Electric Institute
Green Building Advisor, BuildingGreen, Inc.
GreenSpec, BuildingGreen, Inc.
Guide to Resource Efficient Building Elements, National Center for Appropriate Technology
Guidelines for Uniformity: Voluntary Procedures for Home Energy Ratings, Home Energy Rating Systems (HERS) Council
High Performance Building Guidelines, City of New York Department of Design and Construction
Sustainable Building Technical Manual, U.S. Green Building Council
Super Good Cents Builder's Field Guide, Bonneville Power Administration

The *Guidelines* were produced by SBIC and the Green Building Guidelines Advisory Committee. The document was supported by the U.S. Department of Energy's Office of Building Technology through the National Renewable Energy Laboratory (NREL). Special thanks are due to the following individuals and organizations whose assistance during various phases of the project was invaluable.

Early conceptual design:
    Helen English, SBIC
    David Johnston, What's Working

Advisory Committee and Contributors:
    Michael Bell, The Bell Company
    Perry Bigelow, Bigelow Homes
    Eric Borsting, ConSol Energy Consultants
    Charles Cottrell, North American Insulation Manufacturers Association
    Rich Dooley, NAHB Research Center
    William Eich, Bill Eich Construction Co., Inc.
    Tom Farkas, Edison Electric Institute
    Judy Fosdick, Tierra Concrete Homes, Inc.
    Bion Howard, Building Environmental Science and Technology
    Ronald Jones, Sierra Custom Builders
    Michael Kirkbride, Kirkbride Homes
    Lee Kitson, Lee Kitson Builder, Inc.
    Mark Magrann, Magrann Associates

Doug Parker, Big Horn Builders, Inc.
William Reed, Natural Logic
Henry Rogers, Turtle Logic
John Sullivan, Portland Cement Association
Ray Tonjes, Ray Tonjes Builder, Inc.
Brian Trimble, Brick Industry Association
Alex Wilson, BuildingGreen, Inc.

Sustainable Buildings Industry Council:
Helen English, Executive Director
Douglas Hargrave, Associate Director and GBG Project Coordinator
Bambi Tran

Production, Design, and Editing:
Ben Dyson, SBIC
Cynthia Gardstein, SBIC
Sophia Greenbaum, SBIC
Marianne Michalakis, designMind
William Zachmann, SBIC

Thanks also to Dianne Griffiths, John Amatruda, Ric Guilbert, Gordon Tully, and other Steven Winter Associates, Inc., personnel who contributed as part of the U.S. DOE's Building America research program.

Foreword

How we choose to shelter ourselves has an enormous impact on our resources. The millions of homes built every year require a combination of wood, concrete, glass, metal, and other products. These residential buildings consume approximately 20% of America's energy every year thereafter in the form of energy consumption and maintenance needs. But our homes need not be so energy- and resource-intensive. Applying no-cost and low-cost design principles can lower the energy consumption of future housing stock by 30-50%. By applying a whole building approach in the design and development of homes, improved comfort, water-efficiency savings, improved indoor environmental quality, and a more material-efficient home can be realized. The *Green Building Guidelines*, created by home builders for home builders, can help achieve these goals.

The development of the *Green Building Guidelines* has been a collaborative effort of a number of builders, some of whom are members of the National Association of Home Builders, as well as representatives from across the residential buildings industry. The Sustainable Buildings Industry Council members and staff provided the framework with technical support from the U.S. Department of Energy's Office of Building Technology and the U.S. DOE's Building America Program.

The *Guidelines* is a reference manual which will enable builders to easily locate general information. The content of each chapter is presented in such a way that someone new to a topic will be able to understand the concept. Within each chapter, there are also many valuable design and construction tips for more experienced green builders, not to mention numerous references for those seeking truly detailed information on a topic. This approach recognizes that there are many shades of green as well as thresholds for energy-efficient design strategies. Whether or not they are cost-effective, practical, and attractive enough to offer a market advantage to any individual builder depends on specific factors such as local costs, climate, and market characteristics. This is ultimately a decision made by builders, often with their clients, during the design and development stages of each project. The *Guidelines* will be a particularly helpful tool during the early stages and in negotiations with subcontractors, suppliers, developers, and business partners. The materials, presentation of concepts, rules of thumb, checklists, graphics, and other information in this manual will better enable you to achieve the goal of designing and building energy- and resource-efficient homes.

A unique feature of the *Guidelines* is that it is based on whole building design principles and an integrated approach to energy management rooted in passive solar design concepts. A whole building design approach looks at materials, systems, and assemblies from many different perspectives. The design is evaluated for cost, quality-of-life, future flexibility, ease of maintenance, energy- and resource-efficiency, overall environmental impact, productivity, creativity, and ways the occupants will be enriched and enlivened by their surroundings. The whole building approach is intended to broaden your perspective to observe the "ripple effect"—the interrelatedness of all elements of the home.

Contents

Builder's Matrix

	1. Community and Site Planning	2. Renewable Energy	3. The Building Envelope	4. Energy Efficiency	5. Efficient Water Use	6. Indoor Environmental Quality	7. Materials	8. Operation and Maintenance
Land Development	1-8	19-29						
Site Planning	1, 3, 4, 5, 9-13	19-29, 35		76	90-96	99	120, 126	38
Construction Waste Management	14-18		44				109, 110, 126	
Renewable Energy (Passive Solar/PV)	1-2, 10-12	19-40	53	76-77	85-89	105	118, 126-128	135
Foundations		25-26	50, 41-43			99	112-113	135
Framing			43-44				113-114, 121, 125	135
Exterior Finishing		19-24	43, 45				124-127	133
Roofing		30-33, 34-36	43, 45				116, 124	133
Plumbing	4	30-33	43, 50-51	72-74, 80-82	84-96	106	125, 127	134-135
HVAC			43, 46, 48, 49, 50-55, 59-73	57-71		97-103, 127	116, 126	134
Electrical		34-40	50-52	76-84	86	105	126-127	135
Windows		19-25	48, 49, 50-56			103	118, 126-127	135
Insulation and Air Leakage		28-29	46-49, 50-55				116-117	135
Interior Finishes		25-26	43, 48, 50-55				119-120	134
Flooring		25-26	43, 48, 50-55			104-105	119-120	134
Landscaping	4-5, 9-13	20, 21, 23, 24	45, 79	77	90-94			134-135

Overview

The information in this book has been developed primarily for home builders, but it is hoped that, by providing a variety of history, commentary, and short case study examples, others will also find it valuable. The *Green Building Guidelines* provides a series of tips and general design guidance. The book is intended to be national in scope, and as a result, the construction information and many of the example details do not fit all climates or circumstances. The text has been organized to acquaint the reader with basic concepts and provide resources where more detailed information can be located. At the end of each section, you will find "Interactions," references to other sections of the book that describe design strategies, systems, components, or materials that interact in important ways with the topic of the chapter.

Background   The 'Whole Building' Design Process

Home building design decisions are often made one after the other. A subdivision may be laid out without concern for house orientation, a home may be planned without taking the attributes of the site into account, and many aspects of the home may be determined separately, often by separate sub-contractors.

In the "whole building" design approach, every decision is made in the context of others that are related to it. In some cases, one change makes another possible that pays for the first—one classic example is improving windows, which may allow the air conditioning system to be downsized, saving most of the added cost of the windows. The net result is a more comfortable home, which uses much less energy and is therefore greener, at little added cost.

Whole building design takes account of how land development choices, site planning, energy use, water conservation, materials selection, and ultimately, the homeowner's operations and maintenance, all interact.

Avoid Token Measures

One prevalent myth is that it is possible to make a home green simply by adding some energy-conserving measures, equipment, or appliances. While not bad in themselves, such improvements miss the point that there are many aspects of a home to be considered on an equal footing. Token measures also give a false sense of accomplishment, leading builders and homeowners to believe they have done all that is needed, while many other equally important measures have been left undone. Also, any measure that is not properly integrated with the others may actually compromise the performance of the home.

First Things First

It is all too common for one aspect of the home to be designed out of proportion to others (for example, designing an air-tight and well-insulated wall system coupled with poorly installed, low-quality windows). Whole building design encourages *balance* among the measures taken. Many local green building programs help create balance by requiring mandatory attention to all six major topics covered in the *Green Building Guidelines* (community and site planning, renewable energy, energy efficiency, efficient water use, indoor environmental quality, and materials), and not just one area such as energy (important as energy is).

Green Building Key Concepts

1. Building a low-energy, resource-efficient home reduces utility bills, improves indoor environmental quality, and preserves the environment for future generations.
2. People buy homes that are safe, healthy, comfortable, resource-efficient and aesthetically pleasing. These are features that should be marketed.
3. Building in harmony with the environment can bring economic benefits, such as increased property values and lower cost of ownership.
4. Taking control of the specialized services (such as landscaping) involved in green building can provide a builder with new profit centers.
5. Decisions made early in the site planning and design process often have the greatest impact on the cost and performance of the home.
6. A green builder should learn as much as possible about individual products, systems, and components and how they interact.
7. Become expert in meeting comfort needs by using climate-specific, energy-efficient strategies, renewables, and green products.
8. Design for optimal control of water around the site, near the building, and in and through the building envelope.
9. Become a responsible steward of the environment.

The Importance of Energy

While energy consumption is only one aspect of a green home, it is a major concern that must be addressed throughout the design and construction of every project. The Sustainable Buildings Industry Council (originally founded as the Passive Solar Industries Council) encourages builders to design homes and buildings that are *carefully integrated* to consider site, climate, local building materials, and the sun. The Council relies on core principles of low-energy design and the use of renewable (solar) energy whenever possible. However, energy use must be thought of in broader terms than better insulation and equipment. For example, embodied energy (the amount of energy used to produce, deliver and dispose of a product), and energy use during construction (including all those trips back and forth to the building supply store) should also be taken into consideration. An important part, often one quarter, of a home's energy consumption is that from appliances (notably the refrigerator, clothes dryer, and dishwasher), lighting loads, and "plug loads," such as TVs, computers, floor and table lamps, and minor appliances. Many of these appliance and plug loads depend upon choices made by the buyer. Educating your buyers (see Chapter 8, Operations and Maintenance) is important.

State Energy Offices

Alabama	Science, Technology, & Energy Division 334-242-5292; www.adeca.alabama.gov/ columns.aspx?m=4&id=19&id2=106	**Missouri**	Energy Center 573-751-4000; www.dnr.state.mo.us/energy/ homeec.htm
Alaska	Alaska Energy Authority 907-269-4541; www.aidea.org/aea.htm	**Montana**	Planning, Prevention, and Assistance Division 406-444-6754; www.deq.state.mt.us/ppa/index.asp
Arizona	Arizona Energy Office 602-771-1100; www.azcommerce.com/energy.htm	**Nebraska**	Nebraska State Energy Office 402-471-2867; www.nol.org/home/NEO/
Arkansas	Arkansas Energy Office 501-682-8065; www.1800arkansas.com/Energy/	**Nevada**	Nevada State Energy Office 775-687-5975; energy.state.nv.us/
California	California Energy Commission 916-654-4287; www.energy.ca.gov	**New Hampshire**	Governor's Office of Energy and Community Services 603-271-2155; www.state.nh.us/governor/
Colorado	Governor's Office of Energy Management and Conservation 303-894-2383; www.state.co.us/oemc		energycomm/index.html
		New Jersey	Office of Clean Energy 609-777-3335; www.bpu.state.nj.us
Connecticut	Energy Research & Policy Development Unit 860-418-6374; www.opm.state.ct.us/pdpd2/energy/ enserv.htm	**New Mexico**	Energy Conservation & Management Division 505-476-3310; www.emnrd.state.nm.us/ecmd/
Delaware	Delaware Energy Office 302-739-1530; www.delaware-energy.com	**New York**	New York State Energy Research and Development Authority 518-862-1090/3320; www.nyserda.org
Washington, D.C.	D.C. Energy Office 202-673-6718; www.dcenergy.org	**North Carolina**	State Energy Office 919-733-2230; www.energync.net
Florida	Florida Energy Office 850-245-2940; www.dep.state.fl.us/energy/	**North Dakota**	Division of Community Services 703-328-5300; www.state.nd.us/dcs/Energy/default.html
Georgia	Division of Energy Resources 404-656-5176; www.gefa.org/energy_program.html	**Ohio**	Office of Energy Efficiency 614-466-6797; www.odod.state.oh.us/cdd/oee/
Hawaii	Energy Branch, Strategic Industries Division 808-587-3807; www.hawaii.gov/dbedt/ert/ energy.html	**Oklahoma**	Office of Community Development 405-815-6552; www.odoc.state.ok.us
		Oregon	Oregon Department of Energy 503-378-4131; www.energy.state.or.us
Idaho	Energy Division 208-327-7900; www.idwr.state.id.us/energy/	**Pennsylvania**	Pennsylvania Energy 707-783-0542; www.paenergy.state.pa.us
Illinois	Energy & Recycling Bureau 217-782-7500; www.illinoisbiz.biz/ ho_recycling_energy.html	**Puerto Rico**	Energy Affairs Administration 787-724-8777
Indiana	Energy Policy Division 317-232-8939; www.state.in.us/doc/energy/	**Rhode Island**	Rhode Island State Energy Office 401-222-3370; www.riseo.state.ri.us/
Iowa	Energy & Waste Management Bureau 515-281-8681; www.state.ia.us/dnr/energy	**South Carolina**	South Carolina Energy Office 803-737-8030; www.state.sc.us/energy/
Kansas	Kansas Energy 785-271-3349; www.kcc.state.ks.us/energy/	**South Dakota**	Governor's Office of Economic Development 605-773-5032; www.sdgreatprofits.com
Kentucky	Kentucky Division of Energy 502-564-7192; www.energy.ky.gov	**Tennessee**	Energy Division 615-741-2994; www.state.tn.us/ecd/energy.htm
Louisiana	Technology Assessment Division 225-342-1399; www.dnr.state.la.us/SEC/EXECDIV/ TECHASMT/	**Texas**	State Energy Conservation Office 512-463-1931; www.seco.cpa.state.tx.us/
Massachusetts	Division of Energy Resources 617-727-4732; www.magnet.state.ma.us/doer	**Utah**	Utah Energy Office 801-538-5428; www.energy.utah.gov
		Vermont	Energy Efficiency Division 802-828-2811; www.state.vt.us/psd/ee/ee.htm
Maryland	Maryland Energy Administration 410-260-7511; www.energy.state.md.us	**Virginia**	Division of Energy 804-692-3200; www.mme.state.va.us/de
Maine	Division of Energy Programs 207-624-7495; http://bundlemeup.org	**Washington**	Washington Energy Policy Office 360-956-2096; www.energy.cted.wa.gov
Michigan	Energy Office 517-241-6228; www.michigan.gov/cis/0,1607,7-154- 25676---,00.html	**West Virginia**	Energy Efficiency Program 304-558-0350; www.wvdo.org/community/eep.htm
Minnesota	Energy Division 651-297-2545; www.state.mn.us/cgi-bin/portal/mn/ jsp/content.do?subchannel=-536881511&id=- 536881350&agency=Commerce	**Wisconsin**	Division of Energy 608-266-8234; www.doa.state.wi.us/energy/
		Wyoming	Minerals, Energy, & Transportation 307-777-2800; www.wyomingbusiness.org/minerals/
Mississippi	Energy Division 601-359-6600; www.mississippi.org/programs/ energy/energy_overview.htm		

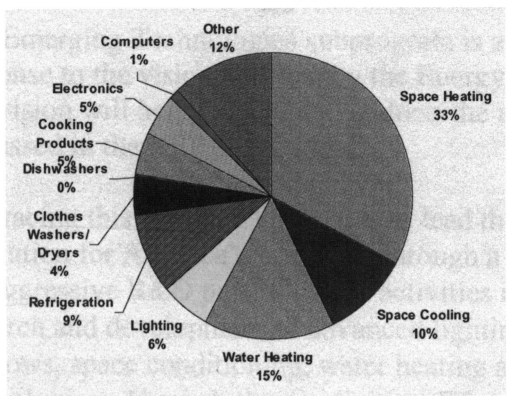

Residential Energy Use for 2000

Source: Annual Energy Outlook 2002, Energy Information Administration, December 2001, U.S. Department of Energy.

Reducing Environmental Impact

The materials and methods used to construct a home all have important impacts on our local, national, and global environment. Using recycled content products made from rapidly renewable resources, recycling construction waste, using sustainably produced materials, and avoiding materials that we now know directly damage the environment help create high-performance, sustainable, and healthy new homes. Siting homes to be climate responsive (whether you are in Miami, Milwaukee, or Manchester), re-using abandoned or infill sites, increasing density (even slightly), and building near existing public transportation are other ways of minimizing environmental impact. Finally, investing more of a building's cost in durable, energy-saving and sustainable materials and in thoughtful details, rather than in raw space, will help builders deliver more comfortable, cost-effective, and delightful homes.

Case Study: Improved Energy Performance Through Design

A 3,000 square foot home built in the Ozark region of Arkansas by a designer/ developer is saving his home buyers more than $850 a year on their heating and cooling bills alone. The couple, Kyle and Christine Sarratt, were not looking for a solar design, but have been living happily in their home for years. The home won the 1997 Energy Value Housing Awards sponsored by the U.S. Department of Energy, National Association of Home Builders, and other partners.

The 3000-square foot Sarratt residence is set into a steep hillside overlooking Beaver Lake in northwest Arkansas. The cost to heat and cool this $186,000 home averages less than $20 per month.

The couple spent about $225,000 on the home ($186,000 plus the cost of the lot), which was immediately appraised at $250,000. The extra air infiltration measures ($500) and unique "ice house roof design"* ($1,500) added a small premium to the price of the home (less than 1%). After a payback period of less than three years, the Sarratts will profit from their efficient home. Most importantly, the Sarratts—who are first-time home buyers—feel that their home's superior energy rating allowed them to qualify for a "stretch" mortgage.

An 80-point HERS rating or above often allows borrowers to obtain as much as $15,000 more than would otherwise be available to them at some financial institutions.

Built on a west-facing slope, the site was excavated to accommodate the views to the west and the sun's energy to the south through a passive solar design. The below-grade walls are insulated foam forms (hollow, interlocking foam blocks) filled with concrete to an R-25 value. Above-ground walls are 2 x 6 construction with R-21 fiber glass batt insulation. The ceiling is insulated with two layers of fiber glass to R-33. Low air infiltration rates were achieved by a house wrap on the outside and a plastic vapor barrier on the inside. Both are taped at the joints and the electrical and plumbing penetrations were caulked or foamed. A blower door test was performed after the drywall went up to expose any undetected leaks. The result was a final tested rate of 0.12 natural air changes per hour. Direct solar gains are provided by 300 square feet of south-facing window area (10% of the total floor area) and are captured by floor tile and the concrete slab. The windows are double paned low-e glass with vinyl casings. The west windows that capture lake views are shaded by overhangs and the porch.

Direct solar gain, obtained through 300 square feet of south-facing windows, provides most of the heat needed. Well-shaded west windows add an open and light feel to the home and allow beautiful views of the lake below.

Case Study: Improved Energy Performance Through Design (cont'd)

The Sarratts' sunny home has virtually no north or east windows.

High insulation and reduced air infiltration reduce the home's heating load by almost 50%. Passive solar heating is the primary source of heat and further reduces loads by another 33%. An auxiliary high-efficiency electric heat pump provides back-up heating and cooling. The Sarratt home's cooling load was reduced by 80% by the passive solar designed overhangs and deck, shading of surrounding trees, ice house roof, and air sealing. Ceiling fans and natural ventilation complete the Sarratts' cooling portfolio.

Visit www.eere.energy.gov/buildings/building_america/cfm/project_ locations.cfm for more information on similar homes.

1st Floor   2nd Floor

Source: U.S. DOE.

* The innovative ice house roof design was used to further reduce cooling loads. This roof design allows hot air to flow through a 2-inch space between the roof decking and a radiant barrier composed of foil-lined panels that are stapled in place between the trusses. The air moves up along the roof line and is vented at the top ridge.

When to Apply Green Building Strategies

It is very important that each green building strategy be applied at the appropriate stage to avoid closing off options. For example, not much can be done to affect the orientation of the house after the framing is underway, but much can be done during the *design* of the home, and even more during the layout of roads and lots. The chart below gives a rough guide for when to consider major design issues, systems, and components.

Appropriate Stage of Design and Construction to Apply Green Building Strategies	
Stage	**Issues to Consider**
Land Planning	Solar access Transportation Greyfield / brownfield / infill Saving natural plants and areas Mixed use Reduced paving Infrastructure Clustering Community stormwater management Wind buffers Wildfire buffers Buffers from undesirable adjacent development Traditional Neighborhood Development Utilities
Site Planning	Wind buffers Porches and decks Reduced site paving Grading and site water management Landscaping and shading Acoustical and visual buffers Basic space layout in home relative to sun (for initial solar access design), wind, and views Septic systems and wells Utility service entries Auto and pedestrian access Parking
Construction Process Planning	Construction waste management and recycling Hazardous waste disposal Reduced site disturbance Site construction access and storage Storage and reuse of on-site excavation and soils
Basic Design	Glazing and solar access Provisions for efficient and energy-saving duct layout Mechanical equipment inside the conditioned envelope Acoustical considerations Design for recycling for homeowners Avoiding attached garage if possible Avoiding excessive size Incorporate natural lighting wherever possible Structural system
Specifications	**Green your specs:** Structural materials Cladding and roofing Insulation Air-sealing materials and systems Finish materials Finishes Cabinetwork and accessories Plumbing and water heating Mechanical equipment selection Electrical and lighting
During Construction	Changes that do not affect other elements and do not increase energy consumption or otherwise compromise green building standards Photograph and record work that will be hidden
Post-construction	"Commission" to ensure proper operation of green building elements and systems "Commissioning" of mechanical and other systems Home Energy Rating/ENERGY STAR® approval Home buyer education and operating manual

Know Your Market

A recent survey demonstrates the disconnect between what builders *think* home-buyers want and are willing to pay for, and what the buyers *say* they want and are willing to pay for. The survey points towards increasingly strong markets for sustainable, high-performance homes that are cropping up all over the United States and gives builders important data about how much their customers might pay, based on the national average cost of a new home.

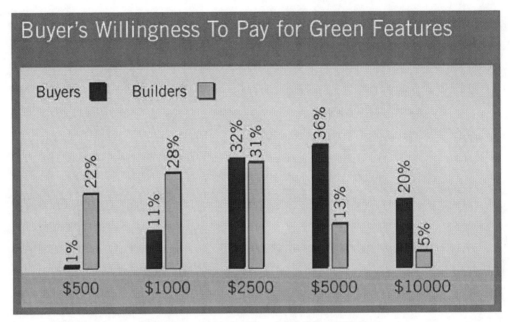

Source: Cahners Publications, *Professional Builder.* 2000.

Having a home rated by a certified home energy rating system (HERS) professional is one way to ensure you have achieved your energy goals and to aid in your marketing efforts. An independent home energy rating in hand adds validity in the home buyer's eyes to your marketing campaign of designing and building comfortable and energy-efficient homes. Participating in a green building, ENERGY STAR® Homes, or other home rating program will also help home buyers identify your homes in this way. You can locate certified home energy raters by contacting your state energy office, local utility, or one of the groups listed at the end of this book.

Different Names for Green

Depending upon what part of the country you live in, you will hear various terms used that are more or less synonymous with green, including "sustainable," "high performance," and "environmentally responsive." Ultimately, what they are all describing is better buildings.

Accessing Local Green Building Programs

In the past several years, builders have become increasingly aware of the need for careful and productive use of this country's natural resources. Home builder associations, state and local governments, utilities, and non-profit organizations have developed a number of green builder programs across the country. Many have excellent resources available to all builders and the general public, not just those in a defined area. Contact them with the technical or general questions you may have. Manuals, workshops, conferences, and other resources are readily available. Green building programs are a great source of information for experienced and novice green builders alike. See the list of Green Building Programs at the end of this book for contact information.

Profit from Building Green

In *Profit from Building Green: Award Winning Tips to Build Energy Efficient Homes,* Jeannie Leggett Sikora of the NAHB Research Center advises home builders on how to gain the inside track to create energy-efficient green homes. Sikora explores topics from marketing to choosing building products. Available at www.builderbooks.com.

Building Green in a Black and White World

Green building is a market for the future. By building green, forward-looking builders can differentiate themselves from their competition and build homes that buyers want.

In fact, you may already be building green and not know it.

Building Green in a Black and White World shows you how to begin building green today. Learn how green substitutes can improve your bottom line and offer your home buyers greater quality and value. You can build green, but home buyers will never know unless you tell them. *Building Green in a Black and White World* shows you how your sales and marketing strategies can promote your green choices and help you to sell more homes to increasingly discerning buyers.

With over thirty years in the building industry, author David Johnston has seen firsthand the change in consumer demands for homes that reflect their values and lifestyles. He knows that green building can become a milestone in creating success and profit in your business.

Visit www.BuilderBooks.com to order.

The Proof of the Pudding

When a home is sited with the climate in mind, its envelope durably protected from the weather and from pests, and its materials and components chosen with care, a new living environment is created. This indoor environment (and its extensions to the outside), where the homebuyer lives, influences occupant health, safety, and comfort. A green home is a wonderful home to live in, and this fact, above all others, provides the green builder both with a marketing advantage, and a personal sense of a job well done.

Chapter 1 Community and Site Planning

LAND DEVELOPMENT

Smart Growth

Community growth and development can be controversial. Issues of traffic, schools, open space, and environmental protection are just a handful of the Smart Growth concerns that home builders and local governments are grappling with.

Many local home builder associations have found that a green building program changes the tenor of relations and improves opportunities for substantive dialogue on Smart Growth issues.

The reason is simple. Green building programs demonstrate that the local home builders can do more than debate an issue.

They can provide concrete solutions to environmental concerns related to residential development and growth. For many builders, the good relations brought about by local government acceptance of the associations' voluntary green building programs has served as a catalyst for a more trusting and less adversarial business relationship on other issues.

Sustainability Principles

Increased density is the most important way to cut the use of resources in developing land. Not only does it reduce the need for certain types of infrastructure and its long-term maintenance, it also reduces the energy consumption of the home by decreasing the exposed surface area in the homes (particularly for town houses, apartments, and mixed-use structures). Properly planned higher-density development, such as the increasingly popular Traditional Neighborhood Development projects, are designed and built for easy access to schools, work, shopping, and public transportation. This type of development reduces automobile use.

Street orientation should be controlled to provide properly oriented buildings whenever allowed by density and view considerations. On east–west streets, homes can be closely spaced, with their major openings facing front and back (north and south). On north–south streets, lots should be shallower and wider, with homes set to the north side of the lot, again with major openings to the north and south. This strategy is unusual, as builders may forget that homes do not have to "face" the street to be welcoming.

Protection and enhancement of natural systems can play a key role in maintaining and enhancing our natural environment. One way builders can help is by configuring development or selecting sites that connect open spaces in ways that preserve or create wildlife corridors of forested, wetland, prairie, or other undeveloped lands. This is far more effective than creating isolated "wildlife islands." Builders can turn these lands into a home buyer asset by creating or planning for walking trails or educational signs and kiosks. Local nature-oriented nonprofits are excellent partners for such efforts. Small parcels of disconnected land or water provide little sustaining habitat for area birds, mammals, and other wildlife and vegetation.

Consider clustering homes and other buildings in a manner that preserves undeveloped lands for use as parks, with or without trails. Builders can also develop sites that promote biodiversity by landscaping using meadows, ponds, trees, and other features while minimizing lawn areas. Implementing these natural environment strategies will add value to nearby homes and ease stormwater runoff.

Access to public transportation is especially important in a previously undeveloped area. Because rapid transit is generally not available in outlying areas, building in areas with high-speed bus service linked to rapid transit or other centers is possible. Developments should also be designed to encourage walking, bicycling, and carpooling as a means of reducing conventional individual auto use.

What is a Traditional Neighborhood Development (TND)?

Traditional Neighborhood Developments, sometimes also known as neotraditional communities, seek to rediscover the principles of small towns built before World War II. Some common features of TNDs are the following:

- an interconnected network of streets to give motorists alternate routes and avoid concentrating traffic onto a single busy road;
- a town center with a small grocery store or convenience store and other essentials (including, ideally, mass transit links;
- formal plazas and greens, the most prominent of which are usually located in the center of the community;
- a mix of uses and housing types in close proximity, usually including detached houses, row houses and apartments and in the town center, apartments built above the stores;
- higher density; and
- pedestrian-oriented design, achieved through the combination of narrow street widths, sidewalks, street trees, houses which are close together—and close to the street—and alleys, which relocate the garages to the rear of the lot and remove the clutter of garage doors and driveways from the streetscape.

Source: www.newtownlaw.com/faq.htm.

Incentives for Developers and Builders

Community leaders may want to consider some or all of the following incentives:

- Waiver/reduction/deferral of fees
- Tax Incentive Programs (TIP)
- Density bonuses
- Reduced setbacks
- Reduced parking requirements
- Decreased roadwidths
- Flexibility in site development standards
- Flexibility in zoning code requirements
- Fast track permitting approvals
- Relaxed development requirements
- Reduced minimum lot size
- Reduced minimum setbacks
- Increased lot coverage
- Increased building height
- Reduced street standards
- Residential development in commercial zones
- Floor Area Bonus

Brownfield Sites

Brownfields are previously developed areas that may or may not have some contamination present that needs to be cleaned up before the site can be used again. Not all brownfields are created equal: some need little or no clean-up, while others may need extensive work. Builders should consider the benefits (typically prime locations and government subsidies) and balance these against the clean-up costs and disadvantages of a site. Examples of successful brownfield residential redevelopment are readily available.

Greyfield Sites

Greyfield sites are those that have been previously developed but are not contaminated. Typical examples are demolished schools, amusement parks, old malls, and at the largest scale, airports (although these invariably contain pockets of brownfield sites). These sites offer the possibility of providing a carefully planned mixed-use development within or close to existing development, filling in a "missing tooth" in the urban fabric and avoiding the development of outlying farmland. In large projects, there are often excellent opportunities for developing sizable wildlife core refuges and linking corridors. A good example of such a development is the abandoned Stapleton Airport in Denver, Colorado.

Scattered-Lot Infill Sites

One way to raise settlement density and avoid the development of open space or farmland is to "fill in" vacant lots. Infill sites are typically more expensive to develop than greyfield sites because they are scattered, access is sometimes constrained, and permits must be obtained one-by-one. The resultant added costs are partly balanced by savings from using existing infrastructure and from local incentives (mentioned previously). Local small builders can typically build on scattered-lot infill sites more economically than larger companies, because they can shepherd permits through the official channels and pay attention to the complexities of building nonrepetitive homes in tight quarters.

Open Space and Building Clustering

Clustering homes enables parks and other open spaces to be preserved for recreational or environmental purposes. Developers have found that they can cluster well-designed homes into a more densely populated community and preserve open space at a greater profit than if they had developed the area in a more traditional manner. Most home buyers are attracted to, and some willing to pay a premium for, homes that are adjacent to open spaces, recreational areas, or other amenities. Clustering can also foster an increased sense of community.

Greenfield Sites

Builders should try whenever possible to build on previously developed land in order to take advantage of existing infrastructure and to preserve existing open space, farms, forests, and recreation areas. Nevertheless, "greenfield sites," or those not previously used for buildings, remain the norm, because they are easier and faster to develop. The principles of sustainable land development mentioned above can help make these projects live up to their name and become truly green.

Paved Areas

Generally, builders should try to reduce paved areas for streets, alleys, sidewalks, and parking lots. It is possible to reduce the paved area in a subdivision by as much as 50% (to 15% of the land being developed rather than the more typical 22-27%). Where paved areas *are* created, consider using pervious materials to reduce stormwater runoff or using lighter colored paving materials to reduce the "heat island effect." In addition, take advantage of recycled materials, such as less expensive aggregates that reuse asphalt and concrete. Planting trees in the parking strips may help reduce the heat island effect.

During the development phase, consider narrower streets to reduce paving materials. However, the reduction in paved area can often only be achieved by adopting incentives that allow reduced road widths and parking requirements. A side benefit is that motorists slow down, allowing pedestrians and children to more safely use sidewalks, lawns, and, in smaller communities, even the street as impromptu community gathering areas.

As always, design decisions require integrated thinking. Here's a simple but interesting example. Most sidewalks are 48 to 54 inches wide, just wide enough to accommodate two people walking past one another at a time. However, designing sidewalks to be up to 72 inches wide could help meet other goals, such as to help accommodate people with disabilities or to encourage children to play on the sidewalk rather than in the street. In any case, consider placing a sidewalk on only one side of the street.

Stormwater Management

Stormwater is defined as precipitation that does not soak into the ground or evaporate, but flows along the surface of the ground as run-off. The management of stormwater involves a combination of strategies to reduce both the run-off and the amount of pollutants that enter the run-off. Federal and state regulations require most construction sites to manage any stormwater leaving the site. Typically the site operator will be required to obtain a permit to discharge stormwater from the site. Check with the U.S. EPA or your state environmental agency. A stormwater analysis will include soil analysis, topography mapping, peak flow calculations, and run-off characteristics. It will also help measure pollutants such as fertilizers and other lawn treatments, as well as vehicular pollutants.

Important aspects of managing stormwater run-off include:

- Minimize land disturbances on the site.
- Preserve existing topography, vegetation, and landforms as much as possible.
- Separate impervious surfaces with turf, vegetation, or gravel to increase filtration and reduce run-off.
- Use pervious paving materials and avoid curbs where possible.
- Use grass paving systems as an alternative for driveways, streets, and alleys.
- Minimize the amount of road salt, animal waste, and vehicle fluids.
- Avoid using pesticides and fertilizers on landscaping.
- Switch from channeling and paved drainageways to systems that encourage sheet flow, thus reducing the need for expensive stormwater piping.
- Use open grass swales, pervious paving materials, and natural vegetation to reduce the total hard paved areas in a development.
- Ensure compliance with local and state drainage master plans and sediment control requirements.
- Make sure to remove or isolate any hazardous material on the site to prevent it getting into the stormwater run-off.

Case Study: Bigelow Homes, Chicago, Illinois

Bigelow Homes outside Chicago, Illinois has successfully created cost-effective, environmentally sustainable, community-oriented developments full of entry-level homes. One of the developments is called Home Town. Home Town uses a number of strategies to achieve its community and energy results. The following is a list of strategies and results used:

- 1,100 homes on 150 acres tripled Chicago's average density for single family development, allowing for the preservation of approximately 300 acres as woodlands and farmland.
- Roads and homes are oriented on an east-west axis, enabling homes to face north-south for optimum passive solar orientation. Only about 10% of the windows face east or west—the least favorable solar orientations.
- Streets are designed to slow traffic down, and sidewalks are widened to accommodate multiple pedestrians and playing children. Homes are designed with larger porches, clear sight lines to the street, and other play areas.
- The more efficient planning of streets and utilities allows Home Town's infrastructure to use only 33% to 50% of the embodied energy of comparable neighborhoods.
- Home Town is designed to encourage pedestrian and bicycle activity by providing ready access to commercial, retail, employment, child care, and recreation activities all within easy walking or biking distance.
- Public transportation is available within the neighborhood and links directly with mass transit and commercial areas.
- Native grasses and landscape materials are used as much as possible to minimize landscaping care.
- All construction waste was recycled.
- Each home comes with a three year, $300-per-year heating cost guarantee (twice the projected annual heating costs).
- Furnaces and hot water heaters are installed outside the air envelope of the house but inside the insulation envelope, promoting both energy-efficient operation and better IEQ.
- Fluorescent lighting is used for both interior and exterior illumination.
- To date, not one complaint has been received about heating or air conditioning distribution or comfort.

Source: Bigelow Homes, www.bigelowhomes.com

Land Development — Rules of Thumb

👍 Contact existing green building programs for resources or information on green building, even if the program does not serve your immediate area.

👍 Lay out streets and lots to maximize desirable orientation for homes in the development.

👍 Cluster homes in lower-density developments to protect and enhance open or wild areas for environmental or recreational purposes.

👍 Reduce paved areas as much as possible, preferably to a limit of 15% instead of the usual 22-27% of land area.

👍 Carefully analyze and plan for stormwater drainage and disposal on the site.

👍 Increase housing density whenever possible.

👍 Include access to public transportation when developing new sites.

👍 Consider the advantages and disadvantages of brownfield, greyfield, and infill sites.

👍 Link natural areas together to create wildlife corridors.

Additional Resources

Green Development, Rocky Mountain Institute, John Wiley and Sons, Inc. 1998.

Lessons from the Field, Northeast Midwest Institute. Offers 20 brownfield development case studies.

Site Planning and Community Design for Great Neighborhoods, Frederick D. Jarvis, Home Builder Press, National Association of Home Builders, Washington, D.C.

Conservation Design for Subdivisions, Randall G. Arendt, Island Press, Washington, D.C. 1996.

Building Greener Building Better, The National Association of Home Builders and the NAHB Research Center, Washington, D.C. 2002.

Web Resources

www.epa.gov/greenkit/4landuse.htm

www.arborday.org/programs/BuildWTrees.html
    The Building *With* Trees recognition program is presented by the National Arbor Day Foundation in cooperation with NAHB. The program outlines tree protection practices and provides builders with opportunities to receive recognition.

www.uli.org
    Urban Land Institute

www.plannersweb.com/
    Planning Commissioners Journal

www.smartgrowth.org
    Smart Growth Network

www.nemw.org/
    Northeast Midwest Institute

www.eere.energy.gov/buildings/plan/whole-building.cfm
U.S. Department of Energy Building Technologies Program on using the whole building design approach.
www.savingsbydesign.com/building.htm
Savings By Design: Whole Building Approach

Interactions

See the following sections for information on how Land Development interacts with other topics:

SITE PLANNING

Green Site Planning in Higher Density Developments

No matter what the density of a development, the site a home occupies determines major aspects of the home's design. For example, in a typical subdivision on relatively flat land, homes are almost always designed with most windows facing the street and the rear yard, with only secondary bedroom, bath, or kitchen windows facing the narrow side yards. Homes are typically designed in specific widths so they will fit on specific sizes of lot with the required setbacks.

As the density increases, the lot and street layouts determine the size and orientation of the homes more and more, until in row housing, narrow plans are developed that only have windows at the front and rear. In these cases, the site planning (except for detailed landscape design) and the amount of solar access is determined entirely during the land development stage. In a typical site plan, the builder should take advantage of the solar opportunities made available during land development, compensating in the detailed design of the home for less than ideal circumstances.

What can a builder do when setting homes in a medium- to high-density subdivision in which solar access and views have been ignored in laying out the lots and streets? Suppose, for example, that the street side of a relatively wide lot happens to be on the west. The simplest measure is to develop home plans with enough flexibility in the design so that some of the windows can be placed on the south side instead of the front or rear and so that living spaces and bedrooms, instead of closets and bathrooms, end up on the south. This may require flipping the plan right to left, or in a two-story home, flipping one story relative to the other (if that is possible). Home styles that feature informal, asymmetrical elements are easier to work with than classical "colonial" homes that emphasize symmetry at the expense of flexibility in plan layout and window placement.

Another approach that works on relatively wide lots is to orient the home sideways on a west- or east-facing lot so that its major facade faces south instead of west (toward the street). In most cases, turning the house requires some ingenious landscaping (fences, hedges, pergolas, etc.) to guide the visitor to the front door. What seems to be a problem can often turn into an opportunity for inventive design, and the end result may prove more interesting than a conventional, street-facing design.

Green Site Planning in Lower Density Developments

As density goes down and building sites become larger, there are more options for locating and designing a house to take full advantage of desirable sun, views, and breezes. Homes can more easily be protected from undesirable sun, views, wind, noise, and rain and snow. Along with freedom comes responsibility, and large sites raise new issues that must be considered during site planning. A large rural site, for example, is not likely to be served by urban utilities, and may need a septic system, a water well, and a long, paved entrance driveway. On the other hand, on a remote site, an array of photovoltaic solar cells may be selected instead of a diesel generator as a source of electricity, with the advantages of being quiet and not relying on any fossil fuel.

Of the wide variety and extent of issues that must be considered to build green on a generous site, some of the most important are the following:

- How the sun moves across the sky at the latitude of the site
- Shading by mountains, slopes, or large trees
- Shading by regular morning or afternoon fog
- Direction of prevailing snowfall and drifting (For example, entries facing northeast in New England can become completely plugged with snow, so New England Colonial farmhouses nearly always had the front door facing south or southeast.)
- Direction of cold winds in winter (so protected outdoor spaces can be located out of the wind)
- Direction of cooling breezes in summer (so the home can be cooled by natural convection without mechanical air conditioning)
- Surface water drainage
- Underground water drainage and soil type
- Existing wetlands
- Attractive car access without excessive grades (especially in areas requiring salt or heating), without disrupting drainage on the site, and with areas to pile plowed snow without damaging native plants or trapping runoff water
- Attractive car parking that doesn't dominate the site and create large paved areas
- Location uphill from the septic field to avoid the need for pumping sewage
- Orientation toward desirable views and away from undesirable present or future development on adjacent sites
- Understanding of soil types and the type of plants best suited to each
- Preservation of desirable plant material, especially true native plants, and thinning or removal of undesirable plants (It pays to have a landscape architect decide which is which.)
- Providing reasonable and attractive ramps or slopes up to the home's entrances, for accessibility

Site Planning for Solar Access

Site planning should take solar access into consideration. Over the years, developers and builders have come up with flexible ways to guarantee that homes have access to the sun for the life of the building. Of course, it is not possible to always provide optimum solar access, so it is important to carefully assess shading patterns to make the best compromise. Subdivisions that have streets running within 30 degrees of east–west will have lots that face or back up to south, which is best for sun control. Subdivisions that have existing north–south streets can consider adding east–west cul-de-sacs.

In northern climates, taking full advantage of solar energy in the design of a home tends to stretch out the house's form in the east-west direction so that most living spaces can be on the south, with service spaces such as bathrooms, garage, storage, and corridors on the north, and with few east and west windows. In southern climates, the same approach to home design applies, because it is easier to control sunlight on a south-facing facade than on one facing east or west. But additional attention must be given to the use of overhangs and landscaping for shading during the cooling season.

Reduce Site Disturbance

When grading, plan activities so that heavy equipment compacts a limited area of soil and stays as much as possible where paving will occur. Prior to construction, develop a site access plan to minimize damage to the site. Indicate areas for scrap/reusable, recyclable, and waste materials, areas for staging and storing building materials, and areas where soil compaction is prohibited. During the construction phase, preserve vegetation by storing materials and performing work outside the drip line of existing trees. Transplant valuable vegetation that must be moved. Stabilize soil during and after construction by using filtration barriers, soil erosion fences, and wood chip mats at entrances. Before beginning construction, save topsoil for reuse and replace the top soil at the end of the construction phase.

During construction, avoid creating erosion by minimizing the steepness of temporary slopes, by planning ahead for temporary site drainage, and by placing runoff barriers and sediment collectors. Silt fences or other suitable methods should be used. Incorporate language into subcontracts to ensure that other trades respect these same rules.

Illustration: Bruce Hendler

Tree Protection During Construction

To help ensure that trees are not lost during construction, consider the following:

1. During construction, the largest single killer of tree roots, and thus of trees, is soil compaction by heavy machinery.
2. The roots of most species of large, woody trees grow primarily horizontally.
3. These roots are predominantly located in the top 12" (30 cm) of soil and do not normally extend to depths greater than 3' to 7' (1 to 2 meters) yet extend outward to an average diameter of 1 to 2 times the height of the tree. As such, tree guards should be erected to protect trees during construction, but since it would be impractical in most cases to establish a complete protection zone, tree guards ❶ should reach at least to the "drip line" ❷ of the tree's crown. This action will minimize root death and the corresponding dieback of the tree's crown.

Landscaping

Careful landscaping can be aesthetically pleasing and may even save the homeowner up to 25% of the home's annual heating and cooling costs (an average of $100 to $250). Design, species selection, and placement of trees and shrubs are the keys to a beautiful, energy-efficient, water-efficient landscape, or xeriscape. Xeriscaping is a landscaping strategy that uses indigenous vegetation that is drought resistant, and once established, is able to survive largely on rainfall and available groundwater.

Consider the following energy advantages when planning a home's landscaping. An example of what an energy-efficient landscape plan can look like is shown below.

Landscaping for Summer Shade
Trees and other landscaping features may be effectively used to shade east and west windows from summer solar gains.

Landscaping Guidelines for Temperate Climates

1. Major glass areas are oriented within 20 degrees of due south and have properly sized overhangs for shading.
2. Ground cover reduces reflected sunlight.
3. Deciduous trees shade east, west, southeast, and southwest sides in summer.
4. Trellis with deciduous vine shades east wall.
5. Garage on west blocks summer sun and winter winds.
6. Windbreak of evergreen trees and shrubs to the north buffers winter winds.

Note: These strategies vary based on the local climate you are building in.

Site Planning — Rules of Thumb

👍 Lower density developments require careful design decisions in order to take full advantage of the green possibilities available on larger sites.

👍 Provide solar access to as many homes as possible during the planning process.

👍 Provide a solar orientation for homes on developed lots whenever possible.

👍 Minimize compacting of soil during construction by keeping equipment on areas that will be paved and by stockpiling topsoil.

👍 Well-designed landscaping can lower a home's heating and cooling load costs by as much as 25% through proper placement and species selection.

Additional Resources

Landscape Ecology Principles in Landscape Architecture and Land-Use Planning, Wenche E. Dramstad, James D. Olson, Richard T. Forman, Island Press. 1996.

Building Greener Building Better, The National Association of Home Builders and the NAHB Research Center, Washington, D.C. 2002.

Design With Nature, Ian L. McHarg, John Wiley and Sons, Inc. 1995.

Web Resources

www.epa.gov/greenacres/
    U.S. Environmental Protection Agency: Green Landscaping with Native Plants

www.gardenforum.com/PassiveSolar.html
    Maureen Gilmer, *Energy Conservation Through Passive Solar Landscaping*

www.nps.gov/dsc/dsgncnstr/gpsd/ch5.html
    National Park Service: Sustainable Site Design Philosophy

Interactions

See the following sections for information on how Site Planning affects other building considerations:

CONSTRUCTION WASTE MANAGEMENT

Why Bother?

The average home generates 3 to 5 pounds of construction waste per square foot, costing builders anywhere from $250 to well over $1,000 in disposal costs. Reducing waste lowers disposal costs. Waste reduction is realized through design and planning. Any money saved by developing and executing a waste management plan can be added directly to a builder's bottom line. By weight or volume, 60% to 80% of a builder's jobsite waste stream may be recyclable (wood, drywall, and cardboard). Metals are generated in much smaller quantities but have good recycling values. Waste placed on the jobsite by someone other than the contractor or subcontractor ("drive-by contamination") can be a factor. The key point to remember is, if you don't generate waste, you don't have to deal with it!

Developing a Waste Management Plan

Effective waste management begins with a company waste management policy and waste management plan. The policy should be a general document that acknowledges waste management as an issue and sets forth the company's general approach to waste reduction, reuse, and recycling. The waste management plan can be tailored to meet the conditions the builder faces in their community, or even on a specific site. It should address the design of homes, material purchasing practices, disposal and recycling costs, availability of outlets, and feasibility of changing worker habits. The plan should be posted on the jobsite, in the office, and given to suppliers and subcontractors. Suppliers, workers, and subcontractors should be informed of its importance. The three basic steps to developing a waste management plan are:

- Identify components of the waste stream and learn conventional disposal costs.
- Understand conditions affecting waste management decisions.
- Establish a plan that follows the waste management hierarchy of *Reduce*, *Reuse*, and *Recycle*. See "Strategies to Minimize Waste Generation" later in this chapter for specific suggestions.

On-site waste reduction is a three-step process: reducing the amount of materials purchased and subsequently wasted, reusing as much construction waste as possible, and recycling whatever waste remains. Reducing construction waste begins with minimizing the amount of scrap and packaging materials. Recycling and waste disposal costs vary greatly from region to region and from month

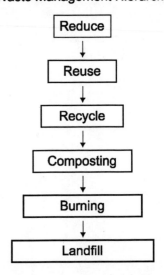

Waste Management Hierarchy

Reduce → Reuse → Recycle → Composting → Burning → Landfill

to month. Builders should note that developing new approaches to waste management can become profitable in the long term on account of changing waste disposal fee structures, even if immediate conditions may not be favorable. Builders will need to evaluate all the conditions affecting their waste management in order to develop the most advantageous plan.

Hazardous Waste Disposal

There are two approaches to active construction hazardous waste management:

1. *Use or switch to nonhazardous substitutes.* An example is water-based paints, which have seen dramatic improvements in performance and price. Using these paints eliminates solvents and clean-up materials that can be considered hazardous. Make sure your painting subcontractor has a waste management plan.
2. *Recycle or dispose of hazardous waste at permitted facilities.* Given the complexity of federal, state, and local statutes, it can be difficult for builders to shift potential liability for hazardous waste materials generated on their jobsites. The largest sources of residential construction materials that could be considered hazardous are waste solvents, paints and coatings, and adhesives. Given the contractor's exposure under federal law, it is prudent to require subcontractor documentation of disposal methods for hazardous wastes or to directly oversee the disposal yourself.

Case Study

Builder:	Bosgraaf Builders
Location:	Holland, MI
House types:	Approximately 55 single-family, detached homes and duplex condominium starts per year.

Approach:
Requires subcontractors to haul their own waste—no dumpsters used on site. Containers for cardboard and general waste provided behind the general contractor's office parking lot. Wood scrap hauled to office parking lot and offered to general public as "free wood." Bosgraaf has also advertised the wood scrap in a local paper and delivered to area residents.

Savings:
Disposal costs totaled approximately $80 per start; the regional average during a 1995–96 pilot program was over $400 per start.

Source: NAHB Research Center's *Residential Construction Waste Management —A Builder's Field Guide.*

Strategies to Minimize Waste Generation

The biggest opportunities for builders to reduce waste are through efficient home design, optimized purchasing, and minimizing packaging materials. These can be incorporated into contract language with suppliers and sub-contractors. On-site, efficient framing techniques and reuse of waste are the best waste reduction opportunities. Wood waste is the single largest portion of the construction waste stream by both weight and volume.

Waste reduction techniques include the following:

- *Reduce packaging.* Packaging can account for up to 25% of a jobsite's waste by volume. Require suppliers to keep packaging materials or ask suppliers and product manufacturers to limit the amount of packaging. Look for materials packaged in easily reusable or recyclable materials such as cardboard.
- *Reduce waste factors* when making material take-offs.
- *Generate comprehensive, detailed construction drawings.*
- *Increase spacing of joists and studs.* This technique can reduce the amount of framing material required by 30%.
- *Create a central cutting area for wood.*
- *Separate reusable lumber,* such as 2x wood cutoffs which can be used for bridging, stakes, bracing, shims, drywall nailers, and blocking. Similarly, cutoff sheathing waste can be used for drywall stops and furring. Grind remaining wood on-site into wood chips to use as an erosion control mat at the site entrance or as mulch.
- *Use cardboard or drywall off-cuts* by grinding up for use as a soil amendment.
- *Require subcontractors to remove their own waste from the jobsite,* rather than supplying a dumpster for their use. While subcontractors may increase their contract price to include disposal, eliminating waste dumpsters from the jobsite eliminates drive-by contamination, facilitates waste separation and recycling, promotes more efficient use of materials, and improves jobsite appearance.
- *Consider precast concrete,* because it creates no on-site waste.
- *Establish set work areas* for each trade, especially framers, to aid in separating and reusing materials.
- *Assign and empower individuals* on your staff to facilitate waste reduction and management.
- *Perform a waste audit* on each job to determine where waste can be eliminated on future jobs.
- *Site-separate waste for recycling* when sorting materials that cannot be reused. Sort into wood, cardboard, metals (wiring, steel, copper, brass, aluminum, zinc), cladding, flashing, plumbing, drywall, glass, plastics, and nonrecyclables. Plastics may have to be further separated into polystyrene, polyethylene, and PVC. Check with local recycling facilities to see what they can accept.

Strategies for Waste Recycling

There are four approaches to waste recycling:

1. *Jobsite clean-up service.* Waste management contractor establishes the service schedule and separates, transports, and tips the material. Fee structures are based on the size of the house.

2. *Jobsite commingled recovery.* Requires builders to put all waste in a conventional container and schedule service for the waste management contractor to transport and tip the materials. The materials are commingled in the container and delivered to a facility that accepts mixed waste.

3. *Jobsite separation.* Requires builders to separate the material and schedule the container service. The waste management contractor transports and tips the materials. Fees are similar to the above two approaches, but savings can be realized through separation of higher value materials.

4. *Self hauling.* Builders handle all phases of waste management: separation, containers, transport, and tipping. Disposal costs and recycling revenues are determined by vehicle cost, tipping fees, and required labor.

Construction Waste Management Procedures — Rules of Thumb

- 👍 A builder's jobsite waste is 60% to 80% recyclable.
- 👍 Create and post a waste management policy and plan.
- 👍 Consider incorporating waste management language into subcontractor agreements.
- 👍 Evaluate and update your waste management plan periodically.
- 👍 Insist that subcontractors cooperate with the waste management plan.
- 👍 Properly deal with hazardous waste.

Additional Resources

Residential Construction Waste Management: A Builder's Field Guide (NAHB-RC, January 1997) presents the cost savings and other benefits associated with waste reduction and recycling of construction waste. Case studies are presented from across the country.

Residential Construction Waste Management: A Coordinator's Guide to Conducting Workshops at the Local Level (NAHB-RC, July 1998) is a companion document to the *Builder's Field Guide.* This book systematically and comprehensively takes readers through the steps, obstacles, and opportunities in waste reduction.

On-Site Grinding of Residential Construction Debris: The Indiana Grinder Pilot (NAHB-RC) is an extensive review of a waste reduction project.

The Regulation of Solid and Hazardous Wastes: A Builder's Guide, NAHB. March 1994. 800-223-2665

Contracts and Liabilities for Builders and Remodelers, NAHB (for hazardous materials). 800-223-2665

Lund, H.F., ed., *The McGraw-Hill Recycling Handbook*, McGraw-Hill, New York. 1993.

The City of Portland, Oregon. Portland Metro, 600 NE Grand Avenue, Portland, Oregon 97232. 503-797-1650

Alameda County Waste Management Authority, 777 Davis Street, Leandro, California 94577. 510-614-1699; www.stopwaste.org

"Examples of Recent Brownfields Projects: Utilizing Solidification and Stabilization Treatment," Wilk, Charles M., Air and Waste Management Association, June 2003. Conference proceedings, Paper No. 69653.

Web Resources

www.cwm.gsa.gov/
   U.S. General Services Administration: Whole Building Approach
www.toolbase.org/SecondaryT.asp?categoryID=34
   Toolbase Services: Construction Waste Management
www.stopwaste.org/fsbuild.html
   Alameda County Waste Management Authority, Alameda County Source Reduction and Recycling Board: Case Study – New Construction Recycling

Interactions

See the following sections for information on how Construction Waste Management affects other building considerations:

Chapter 2 Renewable Energy

There are numerous techniques and opportunities for *conserving* energy in homes. Familiar examples, such as increased insulation levels, multiple glazings, coatings and films, controls and efficient lights and appliances are just a few. There are also a wide range of *design strategies* that rely on the forces of nature (such as the sun and natural breezes) to *provide* heating, cooling, and ventilation to the home. By controlling the sun, we can provide space heating and water heating. By controlling shade and apertures, we can provide greater thermal comfort and occasionally space cooling. Solar strategies can be divided into passive solar design strategies, solar water heating systems, and solar photovoltaic strategies.

PASSIVE SOLAR DESIGN STRATEGIES

The idea of passive solar design is simple, but applying it effectively to homes does require information and attention to the details of design and construction. Some passive solar techniques are modest and low-cost and require only small changes to a builder's standard practice. At the other end of the spectrum, a complete passive design coupled with photovoltaic systems can almost eliminate a house's need for purchased energy—but at a much higher first cost.

In between are a broad range of energy-conserving passive solar design techniques. Whether or not they are cost-effective, practical, and attractive enough to offer a market advantage to any individual builder depends on specific factors such as local climate, costs, and market characteristics.

In the past, the term "passive solar design" has been misconstrued to mean just solar heating. A comprehensive list of passive solar design strategies also includes daylighting, natural ventilation, ground-coupled cooling, and peak load reduction (or shifting) with thermal mass materials such as brick, concrete, masonry, etc.

Following the Sun

One primary benefit gained from the sun is daylight. In northern latitudes and in cloudy climates, sunlight is a precious commodity to be used lavishly. However, the same northern climates where sunlight is most desired are typically also cold climates (an exception being the Pacific Northwest which, like much of Europe, has a mild climate coupled with a high latitude). In cold climates, *minimizing* glass is a high priority, in order to reduce heat loss. But *maximizing* glass is also a high priority, to compensate for cloudy days, short winter days, and low winter sun angles. Clearly, tradeoffs and compromises are called for. Maximizing glass that faces south is a good way to balance these conflicting demands. In southern latitudes, longer winter days, higher sun angles, and more intense sunlight make protection from the sun a high priority.

Ideally, sunlight should be available in the spaces where it is needed, when it is needed. For example, in a northern home, one might try to arrange rooms so that the breakfast area and possibly the owners' bedroom have an east exposure, the kitchen and family room a south exposure, with the dining area on the west. Because the sun is in the southern half of the sky for most of the year in the latitudes of the United States, maximal access to sunlight will typically lead to a design that is elongated in the east-west direction, with as many rooms as possible facing south. This is the classic passive solar home design.

Shading South-Facing Glass

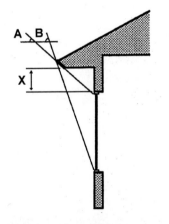

Heat from the sun is desirable during cold weather and undesirable during warm weather. Windows facing approximately within 30 degrees of true south can be designed with overhangs to control the sun (see diagram). Typically, full sunlight is allowed in from mid-September to mid-March (autumnal equinox to vernal equinox). This approach brings in desirable solar heat during the deep winter months (as long as the glass is unshaded by trees or adjacent buildings), but it is a compromise during spring and fall. Because of the thermal lag of the earth, sunlight might be very welcome in mid-March and very unwelcome in mid-September. This is not a serious compromise, because window shades can compensate for the lack of perfection. The alternative, some kind of movable overhang, is seldom practical.

Overhang Projection Factor
The projection factor is the overhang projection divided by the distance between the bottom of the window and the bottom of the overhang.

Because leafless trees can block up to 30% of the sun, they are not desirable on the southern exposure in climates where substantial amounts of solar heating are expected and extra glass is provided for that purpose. But in climates where summer heat is a major problem, trees toward the south can make a substantial difference in the cooling load of the home, especially if they shade the roof. Unfortunately, trees close enough to the house to shade it in mid-summer may become a hazard in high winds and make it expensive or impossible to obtain wind insurance. Again, compromise is appropriate.

Shading East- and West-Facing Glass

It is important to control solar gain from the east and west. The simplest way is to avoid large amounts of glass facing east or west (west solar gain is more problematic, because afternoons are on average hotter than mornings). When this is impractical, wide overhangs, such as those formed by a patio cover or trellis, can shade glass for most of the afternoon. Ordinary overhangs are least effective.

Another approach is to use glass that blocks solar heat. This approach, however, implies that west (and possibly east) glass should be of a different type from north and south glass. Changing glass types on different facades is almost never practical, although solar sunshades can be used with west and east glass, and omitted on the south and north. Again, a compromise is needed between providing the best views, controlling unwanted west and east solar gain, and bringing in desirable solar warmth from the south and north light from the sky.

Windows Terminology

There are three measures applied to windows that affect the control of solar energy through glass. To understand the meaning of these measures, some background is necessary.

First, we are interested in the behavior of the entire window, and not just the glass. To this end, the National Fenestration Rating Council (NFRC) has devised measures that apply to the whole window, and these are the ones you should ask for and use. Most larger window manufacturers use NFRC ratings, but smaller fabricators often do not want to spend the money for the required tests. As a rough guide, you can convert the "shading coefficient" (SC) of the glass to the "solar heat gain coefficient" (SHGC) of the window by multiplying the SC by 0.86. For example, if the manufacturer's sticker shows an SC of 0.60, you can assume that the SHGC is 0.86 x 0.60, or about 0.52.

The Nature of Solar Radiation

Second, we need to understand something about the sun's energy. Sunlight is radiation, the same kind of radiation as radio waves and X-rays, but of a different wavelength. Sunlight also contains a small amount of ultra-violet radiation (UV)—this is what causes sunburn. About half of the remainder is visible light, while the other half is invisible infrared (IR). All this radiation, after it enters a room, is ultimately either absorbed by the materials in the room or bounced back out. All the radiation that is absorbed by the room (including light) turns into ordinary heat (long-wave IR). All of us radiate heat out to our surroundings and absorb heat from our surroundings. If something is hotter than usual, it radiates shorter IR and even visible light (as does a fire) and feels hot. If something is cold, it absorbs the heat that we emit, and this makes us feel cold on that side.

Choosing Glass in Various Climates

Suppose we can have exactly the kind of glass we want. For Example One, in a northern cold climate, we want to let in light from the sun, plus the rest of the solar heat in the IR range. So we would ask for a glass that cut out the UV (because it is not good for fabrics and furniture) but that let in all the visible and short-wave IR that the sun can offer. In addition, it should reflect the long-wave IR that we and our surroundings are sending out, trapping it in the room like a greenhouse.

Now let's move farther south. For Example Two, for north, east, and west elevations we want a glass that cuts out UV, lets in all the visible light, and *cuts out* the rest of the solar heat in the short-wave IR range, because it adds unwanted heat. We want to see out freely, so we don't want to cut out visible light. But we don't want any more heat than necessary, so we block the solar IR. Again, we want to reflect long-wave IR, but this time, we want to reflect back hot outside IR in summer and trap warm inside IR in winter.

Finally, we move to Miami for Example Three, where we want as little heat as possible. The only heat left that we can cut out is that produced by visible light, so we cut out as much as we can stand, taking care not to let the windows begin to look gloomy. Again, we add reflection to keep the heat outside from heating us up inside.

NFRC Definitions

We can now describe the various NFRC measures, and what they mean in practice:

- The *"solar heat gain coefficient", or SHGC* , represents the percentage of *all* the solar radiation (UV, visible light, and short-wave IR) that the whole window lets in relative to a window with a single sheet of clear glass. This measure takes account of the frame, as well as the sun bouncing off the glass when it hits at a raking angle ("off-angle reflection"). The lower the SHGC, the less solar energy comes in.
- The *"visible transmittance," or VT* , represents the percentage of *visible light* that the whole window lets in, relative to a window and frame with a single sheet of clear glass, again taking account of off-angle reflection. The higher the VT, the clearer the window will appear.
- The *"U-factor"* is the familiar measure of transmission heat loss that we use with insulation. The lower the U-factor, the more insulating the window. One important difference between the U-factor of the glass and that of the whole window is the effect of the frame. An ordinary aluminum frame can create a window with a U-factor of 0.60 with glass having a U-factor of 0.35. Put insulating frames around the glass, and you get a U-factor closer to that of the glass alone. So if the sticker does not show the NFRC rated U-factor, don't believe the U-factor unless the window is wood, vinyl, or thermally broken aluminum.

Examples of South-Facing Glass in Various Climates

Returning to our three examples above:

- In Example One, a window for cold climates, we would like an SHGC as *high* as possible. This will certainly result in a high VT, because we will want all the visible radiation, plus the short-wave IR, to come in. We also want a low U-factor to keep the heat in.
- In Example Two, a south-facing window without shading for a mixed climate, we would like a VT as high as possible (for clear vision) coupled with an SHGC as low as possible. If you divide the VT by the SHGC, you get a measure that has no fixed name. We'll call it the "cooling coefficient." The best window of this type today will have a VT of 0.72 and an SHGC of 0.42 for a cooling coefficient of 1.7. If you are designing a passive solar home, then a south-facing window with appropriate summer shading would have both a high VT and an SHGC as high as possible. This can be accomplished with clear insulated glass (SHGC = 0.82) or with a low-e glazing with an SHGC higher than 0.6 for interior heat retention. This is as good as you can do, with more typical numbers being around 1.2 or even less. The U-factor should be low.
- In Example Three, a window for Miami, we would like as low an SHGC as possible, period. A typical window would have a VT of 0.45 or so, with an SHGC of 0.35 or less. Again, the U-factor should be low to keep out the heat.

'Tuning' Glass With Low-E Coatings

Sunlight:
½ Light
½ Heat

Heat is reflected away

Double Glazing

Most of light gets through

Low-E coating on glass

Heat, or radiation, is reflected off glass with a low-e coating.

How is all this tuning of glass possible? It is the result of some chemical magic called low-emissivity or "low-e" coatings. Depending on how many coatings there are, how they are applied, what surface of the double glazing they are applied to, and what kind of metal they are made of, manufacturers have created a bewildering array of low-e glass. They have even made single-sheet low-e glass (the coating can be difficult to clean, so check it out before specifying it). All double-glazed low-e windows tend to have a U-factor around 0.33, providing they have insulating frames.

In practice, major manufacturers tend to stock only from Example Two (south-facing window without shading) and Three glass, for the simple reason that most home construction in the United States is in the sunbelt. If you are designing a passive solar heated home for Example One and Two climate zones, you may well have to special order glass with a high VT and a high SHGC, or find a manufacturer who will fabricate a window using it.

Shading Glass With Overhangs and Landscaping

A roof overhang is a fixed building feature that, when properly sized, helps shade against unwanted solar heat gain and requires no operation by the homeowner. Like passive solar windows, roof overhangs are most effective when they are used on windows within 30 degrees of true south. For east and west windows, consider the use of vertical louvers instead of overhangs. Roof overhangs must be carefully designed to block unwanted sun (typically in summer and early fall), but not block spring, fall, or winter sun that is desirable for heating.

The optimal geometry of a roof overhang on the south side of a home depends on the home's latitude. Refer to the illustration in the "Shading South-Facing Glass" section earlier. In general, overhangs should be designed with a separation between the window head and the underside of the roof (distance X), so that the low winter sun can enter (angle A) and the high summer sun will be blocked (angle B).

Landscaping can help or hinder the energy efficiency of a home. Ideally, landscaping should be used to provide summer shading, enhance natural ventilation by cooling the microclimate around the home, allow winter solar gain and daylighting, and block prevailing winter winds. Locate deciduous trees to shade the east and west sides of the house, but only in areas that are more than 60 degrees east or west of due south from the house. In particular, west and southwest facades should be shaded from low-angle afternoon sun that causes overheating. Depending on glazing location, mixing smaller and larger trees on the east and west side of the house may also offer useful shading, but be careful not to block summer breezes. Other landscaping ideas for summer shading are:

- Vine-covered trellises or patio covers on east and west sides
- Shrubbery or other plantings to shade paved areas
- Use of ground cover to prevent glare and heat absorption
- Trees, fences, shrubbery, or other plantings to channel summer breezes
- Deciduous trees on the east and west sides of the house to balance solar gain in all seasons

Care should be exercised in placing or working with deciduous trees on the south side of a home, because even with their bare branches, these trees can block as much as 30% of the available winter solar energy. Tree placement to block cold winter winds varies with location, but typically means placing evergreen trees on the north, northeast, or northwest facades. See Chapter 1, Community and Site Planning, "Landscaping," for diagrams and more information.

How to Use Thermal Mass

Some heat storage capacity, or thermal mass, is present in the normal construction features of all houses. This is enough mass to support the small amount of south glazing used in "sun-tempered" designs. More extensive use of passive solar glazing calls for additional thermal mass and thoughtful consideration regarding the placement of the added mass. Thermal mass helps prevent high midday interior temperatures in summer or on sunny days in winter. Thermal mass can also be integrated with the mechanical heating and cooling systems to result in a more thermally comfortable house. In a passive solar house, high-performing thermal mass materials such as brick, masonry, poured concrete, or tile are usually placed in the floor or interior walls where sunlight will fall directly on them (this is called "direct gain" or "direct storage").

Most of the concrete and masonry materials used in passive solar design have similar capabilities to absorb heat on a pound-for-pound basis. Thus the major factor affecting performance is the density of the material; generally, the higher the density the better. To ensure cost effectiveness, try to employ thermal mass materials that serve multiple purposes within the home, such as providing structural support or dividing rooms.

Except where thermal mass is directly heated for long periods, it should be relatively thin (generally 2" to 4") and spread over a wide area.

Direct Gain
Direct gain is the most common passive solar system in residential applications.

Mass Location and Effectiveness
Additional mass must be provided for south-facing glass over 7% of the floor area. The ratio of mass area to additional glass area depends on its location within the direct gain space.

Thickness of Thermal Mass

For most thermal mass materials, their energy effectiveness increases up to a thickness of about 4 inches. Mass thicker than 4 inches typically does not absorb and release heat quickly enough to be effective and worth the additional investment.

Mass Thickness
The effectiveness of thermal mass depends on the density of the material and thickness. This graph is for wall or ceiling mass in the direct-gain space. The ratio of 8.3 was used earlier as a representative value.

Ways of Providing Thermal Mass

In most cases, the easiest way to add thermal mass is to use an exposed concrete slab. It can be covered with brick (especially face brick and pavers), stone, or tile, or it can be stained or painted. It is important that it be exposed to direct sunlight and not "insulated" with rugs or carpets. Today's popular stained concrete is an ideal thermal storage medium. A good strategy is to expose a narrow strip about 8 feet wide along the south wall next to the windows where the winter sun will fall directly upon it (assuming the glazing runs close enough to the floor that the strip near the wall is unshaded). Because of its weight, adding thermal mass into the flooring of homes with crawlspaces or basements requires heavier framing, unless the entire floor is structural concrete. Finishing the slab with a dark color gives the best energy performance. A matte finish on the floor will reduce glare as well as reflected sunlight, thereby increasing the amount of heat captured by the mass. If the goal is to dissipate excess solar heat in a hot climate, it pays *not* to insulate under the slab, so that it acts as a heat sink. But wherever the winters are cold, the slab should be well insulated, so that its stored heat is not transferred into the ground under the home. The edges of the slab should also be well insulated. When insulating the slab edge, either by insulation outside the slab or by insulation running between the foundation wall and slab edge, it is important to provide protection from termites, which can use the foam insulation as a route to the interior framing.

For northern climates, storing solar energy is most important during the winter, when sun angles are low. Assuming this low sun is not blocked by trees or adjacent buildings, it can often shine all the way across a room, directly onto a masonry wall. However, as the sun sweeps across the sky, only parts of the wall will be exposed to direct sunlight only part of the time. Therefore, it doesn't matter much whether the wall gets direct sun or not, as long as it gets sunlight that bounces around the room. Thus, a 2" to 4" layer of dense material (brick, stone or tile veneer, or concrete) used to line the walls can function effectively as thermal mass. Increasingly, entire homes are being built out of precast concrete. As long as there is continuous and effective thermal insulation between the outside and the interior concrete walls and floors, all this mass can help store the warmth of the sun. Similarly, the outer walls of a masonry fireplace can help store solar energy.

Case Study: An Affordable, Energy-Efficient Passive Solar Home

We designed and built an 1,800-sq. ft. house, plus a screened porch, for $165,000, well below local costs for conventional custom homes in our area. Wherever possible, the house is constructed of environmentally sensitive materials, meaning they are nonpolluting or low in toxicity and may be recycled. Inexpensive to light, heat and cool, the house should last for well over 100 years with only minimal maintenance. The [homeowners] got what they really wanted: a "green" house they could afford.
—James Cameron and Kathleen Jardine, "Building for Affordability and Energy Efficiency," *Fine Homebuilding* magazine, Houses 1999
www.taunton.com/finehomebuilding/pages/h00002.asp

Case Study: Passive Solar Design

For only $100,000, a couple in cloudy Portland, Oregon, built a passive solar-designed home in their neighborhood's traditional architecture style. The 1,250 square foot home was built in 1994 and saves about $150 per year on heating and cooling bills. When the avoided cost of not having to buy an air conditioner is

The Cunningham/Pinon home blends in aesthetically with the older homes in the neighborhood. The 155 square feet of south-facing windows provide direct solar gain to every room in the house.

taken into account, the home was built at a cost savings. Even without considering that avoided cost, the home was built at a 1% ($1,000) premium: $500 savings on the heating system, $700 added cost for windows, and $800 added cost for insulation.

To optimize the passive solar potential, 155 square feet of glass was placed on the south side of the home (three times the conventional amount for a home this size) under long overhangs that shade the summer sun. Windows on the north and east were minimized and west windows were shaded with elongated overhangs. The home is well sealed and uses added fiber glass batt insulation of

In order to reduce heat loss, north-facing windows are kept to the minimum needed for daylighting and views. West windows are shaded by the porch overhang, which cuts out unwanted summer heat and glare.

R-50 in the ceiling and attic and R-23 in the walls. R-15 rigid insulation can be found under the tile-covered, concrete slab floor, which holds the winter sun's heat.

When passive solar heat is not enough, the home is heated by a quiet, in-floor, hydronic radiant heating system with advanced electric wall heaters upstairs (total cost was $500 less than a furnace with a forced air system). The passive solar designed overhangs, window placement, thermal mass, and air sealing eliminated the need for mechanical cooling. Natural ventilation and ceiling fans provide what cooling is needed. Calculations show passive solar design savings of 50% for the cooling load and 16% for the heating load. An additional 26% heat savings resulted from the extra insulation and lower infiltration rate. Total results: 50% cooling load reduction, 42% heating load reduction.

SECOND FLOOR PLAN

BEDROOM   BEDROOM

FIRST FLOOR PLAN

LIVING ROOM   DINING ROOM

KITCHEN

Other notable green aspects of the home include natural linoleum flooring, low-VOC paints and finishes, recycled carpet, a formaldehyde-free kitchen and bathroom cabinets, and a thermosiphon solar water heater. (The solar water heater savings are not included in this case study.)

Source: U.S. DOE.

Passive Solar Design — Rules of Thumb

- ☝ The increased amount of glazing in passive solar designed homes may add value to the home. More window area offers sunny interiors and better views, amenities home buyers are looking for. Combined with improved comfort achieved by high-performance glazing, this leads to higher owner satisfaction and better resale values.
- ☝ The use of low-emissivity (low-e) glass will improve the performance of almost any home.
- ☝ The energy effectiveness of thermal mass materials generally increases up to a thickness of about 4 inches.
- ☝ Denser thermal mass materials are more effective at storing and releasing heat.
- ☝ Thermal mass materials placed in direct sunlight perform most effectively.
- ☝ If the thermal mass is not in direct sunlight, use three to four times as much area.
- ☝ Do not cover thermal mass materials with carpet or rugs.
- ☝ Select an appropriate mass color. Dark colors absorb the most solar energy.

Additional Resources

The Passive Solar Design and Construction Handbook, Steven Winter Associates, Norwalk, CT. 1998.

Passive Solar Design Strategies: Guidelines for Home Building, Sustainable Buildings Industry Council, Washington, D.C. 1994. Detailed passive solar design information, including climate-specific worksheets and examples.

www.nfrc.org

The National Fenestration Ratings Council Web site provides an industry-standard rating for use by manufacturers. Helpful window selection information is also available.

www.eere.energy.gov/buildings/documents/pdfs/window_selection-777.pdf

For more information on durable, attractive, comfortable, and energy-efficient windows, please consult the U.S. DOE's Energy-Efficiency and Renewable Energy Office of Building Technologies fact sheet, "Window Selection."

Web Resources

www.ases.org

American Solar Energy Society

www.seia.org

Solar Energy Industries Association

www.eere.energy.gov/erec/factsheets/passive_solar.html

U.S. Department of Energy: Passive Solar Design for the Home

www.eere.energy.gov/buildings/design/integratedbuilding/passive.cfm
U.S. Department of Energy: Passive Solar Design
www.sunplans.com/html/passive_solar_overview.php3
Sun Plans, Inc.: About Passive Solar

Interactions

See the following sections for information on how Passive Solar Design Strategies affects other building considerations:

SOLAR WATER HEATING SYSTEMS

Water heating uses about 17% of the energy in U.S. homes and ranks as the second largest household energy expense after space conditioning. To minimize this big energy user, consider installing a solar domestic hot water (DHW) system. They work in all climates, though freeze protection and larger collectors increase the cost in colder, less sunny regions. A typical solar DHW system is sized to provide up to 70% of the annual water heating load. Most solar water heaters operate by preheating water for a standard water heater that, when needed, operates as a backup to increase the water temperature. Thus, the temperature and availability of hot water is not affected and energy is saved. There are two categories of solar DHW systems: indirect and direct systems. Indirect pumped systems can be used in any climate and indirect thermosyphon and batch systems can be used in climates with occasional light freezes. Direct systems are generally only suitable for nonfreezing climates.

Systems range in cost from $1,500 to over $5,000. Solar DHW systems can be very reliable with proper installation and maintenance.

Thermosyphon Systems

A thermosyphon system heats water or an antifreeze fluid such as glycol. The fluid rises by natural convection from collectors to the storage tank, which is placed at a higher level. No pumps are required. If the system heats domestic water directly, water should not be hard or acidic, because it will cause scale deposits that will block collector fluid passages. Indirect thermosyphon systems can be used in moderately cold climates, but the connecting piping and storage tank must be protected from freezing. Direct thermosyphon systems can be used only in nonfreezing climates.

Direct Circulation Systems

A direct circulation system pumps water from a storage tank to collectors during sunny hours. Freeze protection is obtained by recirculating hot water from the storage tank or by flushing the collectors (a process called "drain-down"). Because recirculating hot water greatly increases energy use, direct circulation systems should be used only in those areas where freezing is infrequent. Note that these methods of freeze protection are less reliable than those found in other types of solar DHW systems.

Drain-Back Systems

In a drain-back system, water from a storage tank is circulated through the solar collectors and back to the tank. Heat is transferred to potable water through a heat exchanger in or near the storage tank. When no solar heat is available, the collector fluid is drained by gravity to avoid freezing.

Closed Loop Systems

A closed loop system circulates anti-freeze through a pressurized closed loop. Heat is transferred to potable water through a heat exchanger. The most commonly used fluid for freeze protection is a water–propylene glycol solution.

Batch / Integral Collector Storage Systems

A batch or integral collector storage system uses a combined solar collector and storage tank unit, which is located on the roof. When hot water is used, water main pressure drives warm water from the solar collector/tank to the auxiliary tank inside the house. This design needs no pumps or electronic controls. The heat capacity of the water in the collector is sufficient to avoid freezing during moderately cold nights, but the water in the connecting piping can freeze at temperatures around 32 degrees. A special freeze prevention drip valve should be used on a batch water heater. Depending on how they are sized, batch heaters typically store 30 to 50 gallons of hot water and can supply 15% to 40% of a family's yearly demand.

Design and Installation Recommendations

The performance of a solar water heating collector remains high across a wide range of panel tilt angles and orientations. For maximum year-round performance, the collectors should be tilted from the ground at an angle equal to or slightly less than the latitude. For example, the ideal angle for Atlanta is 35 to 45 degrees, but angles of 20 to 50 degrees are acceptable. An orientation within 45 degrees to the east or west or south is also acceptable. Therefore, collectors may be laid flat against most sloped roofs, as long as the pitch is not too steep and is within 45 degrees of due south.

The Solar Rating and Certification Corporation (SRCC) tests collectors and solar water heating systems and certifies products. Certified products can be obtained from several manufacturers listed in the SRCC Product Directory. Any system purchased should be installed by an experienced solar contractor. Some solar collectors have integral flashings that can be installed into roofing assemblies in a manner similar to skylights.

Pre-Plumbing for Solar Water Heating

Installing solar water heating pre-plumbing allows for easy future installation of an active solar system. Install pre-plumbing if the home meets the following criteria: 1) the home's roof can support solar panels within 45 degrees of due south, and 2) there is space for plumbing between the roof and the utility room or other location where you might locate a solar water storage tank.

The cost of approximately $250 will save homeowners who later install such a system a lot of time and expense. To install the pre-plumbing, run two 3/4" type M copper lines and a 24V control wire down an interior wall from the highest point of the roof that will hold the solar panels to the utility room or location of the future solar tank. Be sure to insulate the copper lines to a minimum of R-6 and to solder all joints with lead-free solder.

Solar Water Heating — Rules of Thumb

- 👍 Always have solar water heating systems installed by an experienced contractor.
- 👍 A typical solar DHW system is sized to provide 70% of the annual hot water heating load.
- 👍 For maximum year-round collection, the collectors should be 1) tilted from the horizontal at an angle within 20 degrees of the latitude and 2) at an orientation within 45 degrees to the east or west of true south.
- 👍 Collectors for any type of solar water heater should be located as close as possible to the water heater tank to minimize the amount of connecting pipe.
- 👍 Systems often require higher maintenance in freezing climates than they do in nonfreezing climates.
- 👍 In most of the continental United States where freezing is possible, indirect closed loop or drain-back systems are often most appropriate. In very warm areas where freezing will rarely or never occur, thermosyphon, batch, or other direct systems may be practical.
- 👍 Consider and develop strategies for the following issues in your solar DHW design: preventing stagnation, providing freeze protection, avoiding calcification and corrosion, and leakage.
- 👍 Consider pre-plumbing homes to accommodate a future solar water heating system installation.

Additional Resources

Solar Energy International, P.O. Box 715, 76 S. 2nd St., Carbondale, CO 81623. 970-963-8855

Web Resources

www.ases.org
   American Solar Energy Society
www.seia.org
   Solar Energy Industries Association
www.eren.doe.gov/solarbuildings
   U.S. Department of Energy: Solar Buildings
www.solarenergy.org
   Solar Energy International
www.nesea.org/buildings/info/solarwater.html
   Northeast Sustainable Energy Association: Solar Water Heating

Interactions

See the following sections for information on how Solar Water Heating Systems affects other building considerations:

SOLAR PHOTOVOLTAIC STRATEGIES

Photovoltaic technology (often referred to as "PV") converts sunlight into electricity. PV produces electricity directly from the electrons freed by the interaction of sunlight with semiconductor materials in the PV cells. PV allows you to produce your own electricity with no noise, no air pollution, and no moving parts. A PV system will never run out of "fuel." PV is being used today in many applications. The simplest systems power many of the small calculators and wrist watches we use every day. Larger systems provide electricity for pumping water and powering communications equipment and traffic signals. Although it is not yet commonplace, PV can be used to light our homes and run our appliances.

The basic building block of PV technology is the solar "cell." PV cells are wired together to produce a PV "module," the smallest PV component sold commercially. These modules range in power output from about 10 watts to about 300 watts. A PV system tied to the utility grid consists of one or more PV modules connected to an "inverter," a device that converts the system's direct current (DC) electricity to alternating current (AC), which is compatible with the utility grid and able to power lights, appliances, computers, and televisions. Although seldom used with grid-connected systems, batteries are an essential component of remote "stand alone" systems. All the wiring and equipment other than the collectors is called the "balance of system," or BOS.

Solar Electric Systems

Power grid · PV module · Inverter · Outlet · Meter

A PV system that is connected to the power grid is essentially a mini-utility system. When a home requires more electricity than the PV array is generating (for example, at night), the need is met by power from the utility grid. When the home requires less electricity than the PV array is generating, the excess is fed back to the utility. Used this way, the utility backs up the PV like batteries do in stand-alone systems. At the end of the month, a credit for electricity sold gets deducted from charges for electricity purchased. If the utility has a "net metering" provision, electricity is sold back at the same rate at which it is purchased. Without net metering, the cost of PV-generated power increases.

In addition to the PV modules, the homeowner must purchase balance-of-system equipment. This includes power conditioning equipment, wires, conduit, fuses, safety disconnects, outlets, and metal structures for supporting the modules. If the system is stand-alone, it will have batteries and associated equipment and may not have an inverter (special DC appliances are available).

Inverters

For normal grid-connected PV systems, the power fed back into the grid must meet the utility's standards of quality. Besides the inverter, which changes the DC power from the collectors into AC, sophisticated electronics are needed to ensure that the sold power is "clean" and in the proper phase.

Orientation

The orientation of a PV system (the compass direction that the system faces) will affect performance. In the United States, the sun is always in the southern half of the sky and is higher in the summer and lower in the winter. Usually, the best location for a PV system is a south-facing roof, but roofs that face east or west may also be acceptable.

Shingle Section

Here are three factors to consider when determining whether your site is appropriate:

Shingle Enlarged

- For maximum daily electric energy output, PV modules should be exposed to the sun for as much of the day as possible, especially during peak sun hours of 10 a.m. to 3 p.m.
- The exposure must be free of obstructions such as trees, mountains, chimneys, other

Shingle Plan

roofs, and buildings that might shade the modules. Consider both summer and winter paths of the sun, as well as the growth of trees and future construction that may cause shading.
- Climate, orientation, and altitude will affect the number of PV modules necessary to generate a given amount of electricity. Seasonal variations affect the amount of sunlight available to power a PV system.

If your location limits the physical size of the system, you may want to install a system that uses more efficient PV modules, which produce more electricity from a given area of collector. The collectors can either be mounted over a roof on metal supports, or, for some designs, can be integrated into the roofing material (i.e., shingles, tile, etc.).

Talk to an Experienced Professional

Consult an experienced PV system designer or system supplier who will have detailed technical specifications and other necessary information. Here are several suggestions for identifying help:

- Check the Directory of the U.S. Photovoltaics Industry, which is posted at the following Web address: www.eere.energy.gov/pv/pvdirectory.html
- Contact the Solar Energy Industries Association for a list of solar service providers (202-383-2600), or visit their Web site at www.seia.org
- Contact your utility company to see which vendors it might recommend.

You will not need to know all the details of designing, purchasing, and installing the PV system when choosing a PV professional. Rely on their expertise to design and install a system that meets the needs of the buyer or homeowner.

Interconnection Agreements

Connecting your PV system to the utility grid will require you to enter into an interconnection agreement and a purchase and sale agreement. Federal law and perhaps your state's public utility commission regulations require utilities to supply you with an interconnection agreement. The interconnection agreement specifies the terms and conditions under which your system will be connected to the utility grid.

National standards for utility interconnection of PV systems are quickly being adopted by many local utilities. The most important of these standards focuses on inverters. Traditionally, inverters simply converted the DC electricity generated by PV modules into the AC electricity used in our homes. More recently, inverters have evolved into remarkably sophisticated devices to manage and condition power.

Financial Incentives

To make PV systems affordable, several states are offering financial incentives through rebates and other programs. These include:

- *Net metering.* Increasingly, state laws require utilities to offer net metering, in which the meter spins backward when the PV system feeds unused power back into the grid.
- *Property and sales tax.* Tax incentives may include exemption of sales tax on the PV system purchase, exemption of property tax, or state personal income tax credits.
- *Buydowns.* Rebates and buydowns, typically based on the power of the system, are a crucial aid in defraying the high capital cost of a PV system.

Remember, the more energy efficient your homes are, the greater the impact the PV systems will have. Measures such as increased insulation and energy-efficient lighting, appliances, and windows will of course drastically reduce your home's use of electricity. The larger the PV system is relative to the home's need for electricity, the more crucial is net-metering to making the system economical.

Case Study: Energy Independence Through Photovoltaics

In 2001 the "Solar Patriot" house was constructed on the National Mall in Washington, D.C., as part of Solar FORUM 2001. During the 10 days it was open, more than 25,000 visitors—among them Congressmen, Senators, U.S. DOE officials, and the head of the EPA—toured the home to learn about its energy-efficiency and renewable-energy features. Afterwards, the Solar Patriot was transported to Purcellville, Virginia, where it became the home of Carol and Alden Hathaway and their three children. The 2,880-square foot, five-bedroom, Colonial-style, modular home was designed and built by Don Bradley, President of Solar Strategies in Philadelphia.

Photo by Don Bradley

The Solar Patriot uses a 6 kW solar photovoltaic (PV) system, which consists of thin film amorphous silicon solar modules integrated into the metal standing seam roof (4 kW) on the main house, and monocrystalline solar panels (2 kW) on the garage. Most of the home's energy needs are supplied by the PV systems. The Solar Patriot connects to the local power grid but is not dependent on it because of its prioritized loads. Since the Hathaways moved into the neighborhood in August 2001, they have been selling "green" power back to their utility company. There have been numerous power outages, but they were unaffected by all of them.

Case Study: Energy Independence Through Photovoltaics (continued)

The Solar Patriot's "whole building" approach relies on passive solar strategies such as building orientation, window location and size, and window shading, which help lower the overall energy load. In addition, the home features a solar water heating system, a geothermal heat pump, added insulation, and other enhancements such as compact fluorescent lighting. As a result, the home requires only 24 kWh per day of electricity, compared with 55 kWh for a non-solar house of the same size.

The total cost for the house was 7% to 10% greater than a conventional home with similar amenities. The Hathaways figure they will break even on the higher mortgage in seven or eight years, and start saving money from that point on. The Solar Patriot and its PV system has produced more energy than the Hathaways use, making it a Zero Energy Home (ZEH). The ZEH concept provides improved comfort, reliability, security, and environmental sustainability by incorporating climate-specific design, passive solar heating and cooling, natural daylighting, energy-efficient construction, energy-efficient appliances and lighting, and solar thermal and solar electric (PV) systems.

Bradley is part of one of four teams working with DOE and its National Renewable Energy Laboratory (NREL) promoting the ZEH concept to the single-family, new-home construction industry. The ZEH initiative seeks to build homes that perform at least 50% more efficiently while meeting their own energy needs. Visit the Solar Buildings Program Web site at www.eere.energy.gov/solarbuildings/ for more information on ZEH.

Renewable and Efficiency Features of the Solar Patriot

Heating and Cooling
- ECR Technologies Earth-link geothermal heat pump system

Fireplace
- Heat n Glow wood burning fireplace insert

Water heating
- Closed loop system consisting of two 4 x 8 Duke Solar Panels
- Hot water loop off geothermal systems as backup

Passive solar strategies
- Direct gain passive design with cement board and tile floors used as mass
- South-facing low-e windows
- 2-foot overhangs
- Cross ventilation with operable windows
- Sun Tube skylight used in second floor master bathroom for daylighting

Photovoltaics
- 4 kW UniSolar thin-film array on standing seam roof of house
- 2 kW array of BP Solar modules on garage roof
- Two Trace SW-4048 inverters
- Eight 200 amp-hour batteries backup
- Loads prioritized in case of power failure

Water conservation
- Low-flow showerheads, faucets, and toilets

Insulation
- R-45 ceiling
- R-24 exterior walls

Other
- Ceiling fans
- Compact fluorescent lights

Source: Solar Today.

Photovoltaic Strategies – Rules of Thumb

👍 Remember, the more energy efficient your homes are, the greater the impact the PV systems will have. Measures such as increased insulation and energy-efficient lighting, appliances, and windows will of course drastically reduce your home's use of electricity.

Additional Resources

Builder's Guide: Hot-Dry & Mixed-Dry Climates, U.S. Department of Energy's Building America program, Joseph Lstiburek, Ph.D. September 2000. A systems approach to designing and building homes that are healthy, comfortable, durable, energy efficient, and environmentally responsible.

Sustainable Building Technical Manual: Green Building Design, Construction, and Operations, Public Technology, Inc., U.S. Green Building Council, U.S. Department of Energy, and U.S. Environmental Protection Agency. 1996. A good section on photovoltaic design and installation. PTI, 1301 Pennsylvania Ave. NW, Washington, D.C., 20004-1793. 800-852-4934; pti.nw.dc.us

Photovoltaics in the Built Environment: A Design Guide for Architects and Engineers, National Renewable Energy Laboratory, DOE/GO publication #10097-436. September 1997.

A Builder's Guide to Energy Efficient Home in Georgia, Georgia Environmental Facilities Authority Division of Energy Resources. September 1999. Southface Energy Institute, Inc., 241 Pine Street, Atlanta, GA 30308. 404-872-3549; www.southface.org

A Consumer's Guide to Buying a Solar Electric System. Produced for the U.S. Department of Energy by the National Renewable Energy Laboratory. www.nrel.gov/ncpv/pdfs/26591.pdf

Institute of Electric and Electronic Engineers, P929: Recommended Practice for Utility Interface of Photovoltaic Systems. Institute of Electrical and Electronic Engineers, Inc., New York, NY (1998).

Underwriters Laboratories, UL Subject 1741: Standard for Static Inverters and Charge Controllers for Use in Photovoltaic Power Systems (First Edition). Underwriters Laboratories, Inc., Northbrook, IL (December 1997).

National Center for Photovoltaics, www.nrel.gov/ncpv

Database of State Incentives for Renewable Energy (DSIRE), www.dsireusa.org/

Web Resources

www.fsec.ucf.edu
   Florida Solar Energy Center
www.nrel.gov/docs/fy04osti/34279.pdf
   U.S. Department of Energy: Heat Your Water with the Sun
www.eren.doe.gov/solarbuildings
   U.S. Department of Energy: Solar Buildings
www.seia.org
   Solar Energy Industries Association
www.ases.org
   American Solar Energy Society
www.solarenergy.org
   Solar Energy International

Interactions

See the following sections for information on how Solar Photovoltaic
Strategies affects other building considerations:

Chapter 3   The Building Envelope

Why the Envelope Is Important

The home's "envelope" separates the living environment from the outside environment in order to provide protection from the weather, intruders, pests, noise, and dirt, to control the entry of sunlight, and, most important, to maintain comfort. The envelope of a home includes part or all of the structure that holds up and forms the roof and that resists lateral loads from wind or earthquakes. This dual role of the envelope is a blessing, because it is economical, and a curse, because its two functions can conflict with each other. A durable and effective envelope is a key element in a green home, because all that goes on within the home depends on its proper functioning.

What Does the Envelope Include?

In this chapter and in Chapter 7, Materials, the envelope is subdivided as follows:

- Foundations
- Walls and floors
- Wall cladding/exterior surfaces
- Roofs
- Insulation and air sealing
- Windows

In a typical one-story home on a concrete slab, the envelope includes the slab, the outside walls, and the trussed roof structure that spans between the walls. If the wall structure is concrete or masonry, it is likely to be covered with stucco or brick on the exterior, with insulation and gypsum board on the inside.

If the wall structure is framed, the framing can be either wood or steel. Insulation is placed between the framing members. In most steel-framed homes (and many wood-framed homes), an additional layer of insulation occurs either inside or, more commonly, outside the framing. The outside surface will be cladding (brick, stone, wood, wood composites, etc.) along with an air barrier and/or water resistant material such as asphalt paper or housewrap, while gypsum board and possibly a vapor retarder occur on the inside surface.

In a typical two-story home with a basement or crawlspace, the envelope includes the foundation walls and the insulated edges of the floor structures in addition to the walls and roof. At the roof, the weather-protective roofing and the energy-protective layer of attic insulation are separate from each other. In some cases, the roof insulation occurs directly under the roof, creating a cathedral ceiling over usable space, or a "cathedralized" ceiling when insulation is placed at roof level in a trussed roof.

Building Science in Transition

Building science is crucial in understanding how homes work. Long-held theories and ideas are being challenged, and accurate data is flowing in from well-instrumented test sites and from field monitoring of new and existing homes. Building scientists seldom disagree about the facts. Controversy arises over how much emphasis to give each of the many factors that influence the behavior of building elements. For example, one investigator may approve of a technique because it has beneficial consequence X, while another investigator will disapprove of the same technique because it has undesirable consequence Y. Both X and Y occur, so both investigators are correct. But which is more important, the good result X or the bad result Y? How much X and how much Y actually occur in the field?

Adding to the controversy, some building code provisions (for example, crawlspace ventilation) are based on outdated theories coupled with sparse evidence drawn from building construction technology no longer in use. Yet, because these requirements have been an important feature of the building codes used by two generations of designers, builders, and investigators, they seem sacrosanct. It should not be a surprise that dislodging old ideas in favor of newer, more solidly based findings may take several years of discussion, compromise, and education.

Foundations

Where the frostline is relatively deep, homes are typically built on crawlspaces or basements. If a basement is not needed or desired, either a slab or crawlspace is used. Crawlspaces have a serious disadvantage: they are seldom visited for inspection, so a leak (either from inside or from outside) can remain undetected for weeks or months, encouraging the growth of mold or wood-rot fungus. Provided it is insulated at the perimeter, a slab on grade eliminates this problem. It also has many other advantages in colder climates, including its ability to store and release solar-generated heat, and if properly insulated below, to form an ideal substrate for radiant heating.

In colder climates, most builders find it easier to build a floor over a crawlspace than to carefully backfill for a slab. The first of these problems can be resolved by erecting the bearing walls on strip foundations independent of the slab, which can then be poured after the home is closed in. The second can be overcome by using a frost-protected shallow foundation (FPSF), where a skirting of insulation is placed around the outside of the foundation, trapping ground heat and making deep frostwalls unnecessary. These foundations are described more fully in Chapter 7, Materials.

If a basement is present, heating equipment and piping or ductwork is invariably located in the basement. Heat loss from basements therefore becomes an important part of the home's energy consumption. Achieving a high rating in most Home Energy Rating programs requires that the basement be sealed and insulated and that walls be insulated whenever a basement is converted to living space. One technology that automatically insulates the basement wall very effectively is insulating concrete forms (ICF), where concrete is poured into modular forms made of foam insulation. These are more fully discussed in Chapter 7, Materials.

Moisture Control Techniques

Careful attention to water movement (foundation drainage systems, house perimeter grading, and flashing details) and vapor movement (air sealing details and vapor barrier systems) can go a long way toward controlling moisture and possible mold problems in homes. The following is a list of general techniques to help control moisture:

Kickout flashing sends water away from the sidewall of a building where a roof abuts a wall. (Photo courtesy of Raintek)

- Direct downspout discharge well away from the foundation.
- Grade away from the house a minimum of 6 inches in the first 10 feet.
- Learn where seasonal high ground water occurs, and do not build basement slabs, floor slabs, or crawlspace floors less than 1 foot above high groundwater (or install a fail-safe pumping system).
- Footing drains should drain to daylight, a drywell, or a sump pump.
- Install a puncture-resistant polyethylene vapor retarder directly beneath a floor slab.
- Install a capillary moisture break between the top of the footing and the foundation wall (or under a footing that is integral with the slab).
- Install a gravel bed below slab-on-grade floors.
- Use "rainscreen" cladding in all cases where sealing at the surface cannot be guaranteed to stop all water.
- Use kickout flashing where an eave runs into a sidewall.
- Avoid valleys and keep chimneys, dormers, and skylights away from valleys.
- Use substantial crickets where water might not flow easily off the roof.

Walls and Floors

As dimensional lumber becomes scarcer, the wood framing needed to produce straight and true walls and floors is becoming harder to find and more expensive. One alternative is to use engineered lumber, which is made from scraps, strips, layers, or shreds of wood held together by glue or by glued finger-joints. For example, plywood sheathing has been replaced by OSB sheathing in nearly every part of the country. Another alternative is steel framing, which is light in weight, straight, and unaffected by moisture.

A third is structural masonry, poured-in-place concrete, or precast concrete. All these options are discussed in Chapter 7, Materials.

Other alternatives to conventional wall construction include structural insulated panels (SIPs), where typically a layer of expanded polystyrene (EPS) foam is sandwiched between two layers of OSB, and insulating concrete forms, where concrete is poured into EPS foam forms that stay in place to create a tightly sealed, well-insulated wall.

Floors made with engineered lumber joists, or with finger-jointed or gang-nailed trusses, have many advantages in addition to their green attributes. By allowing ductwork and piping to run through them, they encourage the practice of keeping ducts and pipes inside the conditioned envelope.

Framing Efficiency

Efficient framing techniques require fewer materials and generate less waste during construction. Rough framing accounts for about 15% to 20% of the total cost of typical home construction. Using proven techniques to reduce the amount of framing material can lower costs, better utilize resources, and save labor.

Optimum value engineering (OVE). OVE or advanced framing uses engineering principles to minimize material usage while meeting model building code structural performance requirements. OVE techniques include the following:

- Increasing wall stud spacing to 24 inches on-center, rather than the standard 16 inches
- Spacing floor joists and roof rafters at 24 inches instead of 16 inches
- Using in-line framing when floor, wall, and roof framing members are in line with one another—sometimes called "in-line" or "stack" framing (in this manner, loads are transferred directly from one bearing member to the next, thus creating a direct load path and a more efficient structure)
- Designing homes on 2-foot modules, thereby reducing waste and installation labor, since most panel products come in even-incremented dimensions such as 4' x 8'
- Using two-stud corner framing instead of three studs, and replacing two- and three-stud backing for drywall attachments at wall 'T' intersections with inexpensive drywall clips or scrap lumber
- Properly sizing headers, such as using doubled 2 x 4s, 6s, and 8s over smaller door and window openings instead of doubled 2 x 10s
- Eliminating headers in nonloadbearing walls

Substitute 2 x 6 for conventional 2 x 4 framing. 2 x 6 framing at 24" on-center uses roughly the same amount of board-feet of lumber as 2 x 4 lumber at 16" on-center, while leaving a larger wall cavity for increased insulation levels. Once framing crews have gained experience, these techniques can save money by using fewer pieces and being faster to assemble.

Wall Cladding/Exterior Surfaces

Wall cladding (siding) needs to be installed and flashed to manage rainwater. Water typically penetrates through the outer cladding, either by suction (capillary action) or at joints and cracks. It is possible in some cases to seal the home against moisture intrusion at its outside surface, as for example poured concrete walls with an integral stucco finish. More commonly, the outer cladding sheds most of the water, but the real surface that must be sealed from rain occurs at an inner layer that is separated from the outer cladding by an air space. This technique is called "rainscreen" construction. Typical examples are brick, vinyl siding, and EIFS. In the last case, failures of caulking around windows led to the development of rainscreen EIFS designs. In rainscreen wall construction, the inner water-resistant barrier must be carefully flashed around all penetrations, especially around windows and doors. A very important technique is to install a "flashing pan" under all windows. There are new peel-and-stick flashing materials that make this task easier.

Roofs

Whether a roof is framed or is trussed, and whether roofing is asphalt, metal, or tile, there are principles that should be followed to minimize the chances of failure leading to water intrusion. Rainwater collects in valleys, and these concentrations increase the chances for water to run up under the roofing at those locations. If you have valleys in the roof, make sure water can flow unimpeded for several feet on either side of the valley. Don't place a dormer or chimney in or near the valley, and don't place dormers close together. When there is an obstruction such as a chimney, or where a "blind" valley occurs between two parallel roofs, there needs to be a substantial cricket that directs water around the obstruction or out of the blind valley. Where an eave ends against a wall, kick-out flashing is needed to prevent water that runs down the joint between wall and roof from penetrating and running behind the siding below.

The living space should be carefully air sealed from the attic or cathedral ceiling to prevent warm, humid interior air from wetting the roof structure in cold weather. Roof ventilation is another topic under intense scrutiny by the building science community, with the final word on the subject yet to be decided. Investigators are experimenting with various methods of reducing attic duct losses or gains: burying the ducts under attic insulation, insulating the home directly under the roof and at the gable end walls, or building a sealed duct plenum into the truss structure. Trusses are widely used in home building. They have the green advantage of using small-dimension and short lengths of lumber. Light-colored asphalt shingles or shiny light-colored painted metal or glazed tile roofing can help reduce attic temperatures.

Insulation and Air Sealing

There are many types of insulation available to the builder, some of which are described in Chapter 7, Materials. Some building systems, such as SIPs, insulating concrete forms (ICFs), and shallow frost-protected foundations (SFPF) include insulation as an integral part of the system. In the open cavities of framed walls, there are many choices.

Fiber Glass Insulation. Fiber glass insulation has natural fire resistance and generally has 20-25% recycled content, including both post-industrial glass cullet and post-consumer recycled bottles. Some products go up to 40% recycled content. These levels meet the EPA Buying Guidelines in terms of recycled content. Fiber glass is made from glass cullet and sand, which are widely available, rapidly renewable resources, and uses minimal packaging. Fiber glass insulation is used in walls, ceilings, and cavities in the form of batts, blankets, and loose fill.

State-of-the-art soft foam insulation is sprayed into walls, floors, and ceilings.

Many manufacturers have certified their products to the GREENGUARD® specification, and fiber glass products are available with or without formaldehyde binders. The Consumer Products Safety Commission has concluded that the amount of formaldehyde present in fiber glass is not a concern. See Chapter 6, Indoor Environmental Quality, for more information on air sealing and duct work.

Cellulose Loose-Fill Insulation. Cellulose loose-fill insulation is made from wastepaper, such as used newsprint and boxes, that is shredded and pulverized into small fibrous particles. Chemicals are then added to provide resistance to fire and insects. In many cases, cellulose is labeled with both "settled

Vapor Retarders

Humidity in the air can move through ordinary building materials by a process called "osmosis." In the past 50 years, a strong emphasis on osmosis has led to the almost universal requirement for a strongly effective vapor retarder. Recently, this emphasis has been re-examined in light of condensation problems in air-conditioned homes in hot–humid climates, where an interior vapor retarder contributes to the moisture problems rather than solving them.

Air and water leakage, not osmosis, is the primary cause of moisture damage in walls and attics. Once air leakage is controlled by air sealing and water leakage is controlled by proper water management techniques, the vapor retarder can be chosen to suit a specific climate.

thickness" and "installed thickness." To ensure thermal performance, it is essential to follow the manufacturer's guidance for installed thickness, so that proper R-value is achieved. Loose-fill insulation can be easier to fit around pipes and other obstructions in a wall assembly. Cellulose is sometimes applied in a wetspray form. Care should be taken to allow for appropriate drying time based on both temperature and humidity levels.

CFC-Free Spray Foam Insulation. Foam insulation has excellent air-sealing qualities, moisture resistance, and insulating properties. Choose foam insulation products that use a lower ozone-depleting blowing agent such as HCFCs (hydrochlorofluorocarbons), HFCs (hydrofluorocarbons), or better yet, CO_2, pentane, and isobutene.

Mineral Wool Insulation. When installing insulation to a high-temperature surface, mineral wool is ideal. It is also used as passive fire protection. Mineral wool comes in board, blanket and loose fill forms. Many types of mineral wool insulation have recycled content as high as 70%. Slag wool insulation contains as much as 90% recycled blast furnace slag, some of which is reclaimed from landfills for use in insulation.

Besides the very common batts and rolls of fiber glass, there are batts made of cotton or rock wool. Cellulose, fiber glass, and rock wool can all be sprayed into open wall cavities. If not allowed to dry thoroughly before enclosing, wet-applied products may support mold growth and damage other building materials with which they come into contact. If the cavities are covered by netting or polyethylene, fiber glass, cellulose, or rock wool, or are completely inert, aerated cement can be blown in through holes cut in the closure material.

Foam-in-place insulation is typically either high-density or low-density polyurethane. Foam can be sprayed directly into cavities, either filling them or creating an air-sealing liner over which batts can be placed. Foams have the advantage that they can be sprayed into overhead cavities, creating an air-sealed cocoon around the living space. They can also be sprayed directly on concrete or masonry. Where rigid board is needed, polyisocyanurate is available with impervious skins on both sides, while unfaced expanded polystyrene (EPS) and extruded polystyrene (XPS) are both widely available in a variety of thicknesses and sizes. Because foam can be more expensive to install, a hybrid system in which foam is applied to the sheathing and then covered with a fiber glass batt can be an alternative.

Exposed or Unexposed? When installing insulation materials in occupied or unoccupied spaces, be aware of the building code requirements for flame spread and smoke-developed indices. These code requirements will dictate whether materials such as vapor retarders and insulation can be left exposed or must be covered by a fire-resistive barrier.

Air Leakage Driving Forces

Requirements for air leakage to occur are:

1. *Holes.* The larger the hole, the greater the air leakage. Large holes have higher priority for air sealing efforts.
2. *Driving force.* A pressure difference that forces air to flow through a hole. Holes that experience stronger and more continuous driving forces have higher priority.

The common driving forces are:

1. *Wind.* Caused by weather conditions.
2. *Stack effect.* Upward air pressure due to the buoyancy of air.
3. *Mechanical blower.* Induced pressure imbalances caused by operation of fans and blowers.

Wind is usually considered to be the primary driving force for air leakage, but this depends on how tight the house is. When the wind blows against a building, it creates a high pressure zone on the windward areas. Outdoor air from the windward side infiltrates into the building while air exits on the leeward side. Wind acts to create areas of differential pressure, which cause both infiltration and exfiltration. The degree to which wind contributes to air leakage depends on its velocity and duration.

The temperature difference between inside and outside causes warm air inside the home to rise while cooler air falls, creating a driving force known as the *stack effect.* In homes with large holes in the attic and crawlspace or basement, the stack effect can be a major contributor to air leakage, moisture, and air quality problems.

Poorly designed and installed forced-air systems can create strong pressure imbalances inside the home whenever the heating and cooling system operates. In addition, unsealed ductwork located in attics and crawlspaces can draw pollutants and excess moisture into the home. Correcting duct leakage problems is critical when constructing an energy-efficient home.

Wind Driven Infiltration

On average, wind in the Southeast creates a pressure difference of 10 to 20 Pascals on the windward side. However, most homes have only small cracks on the exterior.

The Stack Effect

The stack effect can create pressure differences between 1 to 3 Pascals due to the power of rising warm air. Crawl space and attic holes are often large.

Mechanical System Driven Infiltration

Leaks in supply and return ductwork can cause pressure differences of up to 30 Pascals. Exhaust equipment such as kitchen and bath fans and clothes dryers can also create pressure differences.

Air Infiltration Control

This is a brief overview of the many infiltration issues that arise when constructing an energy-efficient house. Sealing the house carefully to reduce air infiltration is as necessary as adding insulation. Consider the following:

- In cold climates, it is generally safe to wrap the inside of a home that is *not air conditioned* with most types of "vapor retarders."
- The preferred strategy for an air conditioned home in a cold climate is to caulk every leakage path and use a moderately effective vapor retarder, such as the kraft paper facing on batt insulation.
- In hot and humid climates, it is essential to avoid any sort of vapor retarder on the inside surface so that when the wall or ceiling gets wet, it can dry out to the air conditioned interior.
- Make sure all wall cavities are well sealed to minimize air leakage, or fill the cavity with sprayed-on insulation. Avoid wet-spray cellulose, unless measurements are made to guarantee that it has dried out before applying interior finishes, a process that can take days.
- Perhaps the most important point to remember about gap sealing is that the amount of movement expected in the joint determines the width and design of the seal. In general even the most expensive sealant will not expand or contract more than half its width. The back of a sealant bead should not be in contact with the materials it joins so it can flex properly.
- Perform prescriptive air sealing to control infiltration at the most common sources: floor-wall junctions (sillplates), wall outlets, windows and window openings, HVAC ducts, fireplaces, recessed lighting fixtures (see Chapter 4, Energy Efficiency), and exterior venting devices for bathrooms, kitchens, and laundry rooms. Careful caulking in these areas will reduce infiltration and control moisture. The cost of air sealing to a moderate level of about 0.3 ach natural is between $250 and $500.
- Installing house wrap or building paper as air barriers over the exterior sheathing will reduce air and moisture penetrations. Ensure proper installation by taping all seams and wrapping and/or taping at penetrations such as windows, doors, vents, etc.

See "Gap Sealing Checklist for Homes" on the next page for details of where and how to gap seal.

Air Infiltration Control Checklist

Typical Home Air Leakage Sites

1. *Slab floors:* Seal all holes in the slab to prevent entry of water vapor and soil gas. A vapor retarder beneath the slab will reduce water vapor transmissions.
2. *Sill plate and rim joist:* Seal sill plates in basements and unvented crawl-spaces. Caulk or gasket rim or band joists between floors in multi-story construction.
3. *Bottom plate:* Use either caulk or gasket between the plate and subflooring.
4. *Subfloor:* Use an adhesive to seal the seams between pieces of subflooring.
5. *Electrical wiring:* Use wire-compatible caulk or spray foam to seal penetrations.
6. *Electrical boxes:* Use approved caulk to seal wiring on the outside of electrical boxes. Seal between the interior finish material and boxes.
7. *Electrical box gaskets:* Caulk foam gaskets to all electrical boxes in exterior and interior walls before installing coverplates.
8. *Recessed light fixtures:* Consider using surface-mounted light fixtures rather than recessed lights. When used, specify airtight models rated for insulation coverage (IC).
9. *Exhaust fans:* Seal between the fan housing and the interior finish material. Choose products with tight-fitting backdraft dampers.
10. *Plumbing:* Locate plumbing in interior walls, and minimize penetrations. Seal all penetrations with foam sealant or caulk.
11. *Attic access:* Weatherstrip attic access openings. For pull-down stairs, use latches to hold the door panel tightly against the weatherstripping. Cover the attic access opening with an insulated box.
12. *Whole house fan:* Use a panel made of rigid insulation or plastic to seal the interior louvers when not in use.
13. *Flue stacks:* Install a code-approved flue collar and seal with fire-rated caulk.
14. *Combustion appliances:* Closely follow local codes for firestopping measures, which reduce air leakage as well as increase the safety of the appliance. Make certain all combustion appliances, such as stoves and fireplaces, have an outside source of combustion air and tight-fitting dampers or doors.
15. *Return and supply registers:* Seal all boots connected to registers or grilles to the interior finish material.
16. *Ductwork:* Seal all joints in supply and return duct systems with mastic.
17. *Air handling unit* (for heating and cooling system): Seal all cracks and unnecessary openings with mastic. Seal service panels with tape.
18. *Dropped ceiling soffit:* Use sheet material and sealant to stop air leakage from attic into the soffit or wall framing, then insulate.
19. *Chases* (for ductwork, flues, etc.): Prevent air leakage through these bypasses with sheet materials and sealants.

Air Infiltration Control Diagrams

Sealing Bypasses

Plumbing - Seal penetrations, especially under bathtubs and other fixtures. Install drywall, plastic, or housewrap behind bathtub to provide an air barrier.

Dropped Ceiling Soffit - If kitchen cabinets or bath/shower enclosures have dropped soffits, provide a continuous seal at the attic floor.

Air Infiltration Control Diagrams (continued)

Sealing Bypasses for Flues and Ductwork

Chases - Framed chases for flues should be sealed at the attic floor. Use a continuous layer of plywood or other solid sheet-good. Seal between the flue and combustible materials with fire-rated caulk and a noncombustible flue collar.

Return and Supply Plenums - Seal framed areas for ductwork.

Windows

Windows play a crucial role in creating an energy-efficient envelope. How they are installed and flashed is crucial to maintaining the moisture integrity of the walls, as discussed above. Flashing around windows should carefully overlap the upper layer over the lower one in all cases. Do not rely upon window flanges set in sealant to keep water out, and use flashing pans whenever possible. References are given that describe proper window flashing in detail.

Awning   Hopper   Sliding

Fixed   Double-hung   Casement

Energy-efficient windows come in traditional styles.

The Building Envelope — Rules of Thumb

- 👍 Consider advanced framing to reduce framing costs, add strength to a home's envelope, and reduce material consumption.
- 👍 Pay careful attention to water movement and vapor movement.
- 👍 Install a "flashing pan" under all windows.
- 👍 Use the "Gap Sealing Checklist" for your homes.
- 👍 Stay abreast of rapidly changing building science and codes regarding crawlspace and roof ventilation and vapor retarders.
- 👍 Consider advanced foundation systems such as FPSFs and ICFs.

Additional Resources

Builder's Guide: Hot-Dry and Mixed-Dry Climates. Office of Building Technology, State and Community Programs, Energy Efficiency and Renewable Energy, U.S. Department of Energy. 2000.

"Advanced Wall Framing," *Technology Fact Sheet,* Office of Building Technology, State and Community Programs, Energy Efficiency and Renewable Energy, U.S. Department of Energy. October 2000. 800-DOE-3732; www.eere.energy.gov/

GreenSpec: The Environmental Building News Product Directory and Guideline Specifications, Dwight Homes, Larry Strain, AIA, Alex Wilson, and Sandra Leibowitz. BuildingGreen, Inc., Brattleboro, Vermont. 4th Edition. www.greenspec.com

Guide to Resource Efficient Building Elements, Mumma, Tracy. National Center for Appropriate Technology's Center for Resourceful Building Technology, Missoula, Montana. www.crbt.org

Building Greener Building Better, The National Association of Home Builders and the NAHB Research Center, Washington, D.C. 2002.

Web Resources

www.efficientwindows.org
   U.S. Department of Energy: Efficient Windows Collaborative
www.pathnet.org
www.toolbase.org
www.ecco.org
   The Environmental Council of Concrete Organizations provides bulletins on using concrete as part of a sustainable environment. 800-994-3226
www.greenbuilder.com/sourcebook/
   The city of Austin's Green Building Network materials sourcebook.
www.nfrc.org
   The National Fenestration Ratings Council Web site provides an industry-standard rating for use by manufacturers. Helpful window selection information is also available.
www.eere.energy.gov/buildings/documents/pdfs/window_selection-777.pdf
   For more information on durable, attractive, comfortable, and energy-efficient windows, please consult the U.S. DOE's Energy-Efficiency and Renewable Energy Office of Building Technologies fact sheet, "Window Selection."
www.ornl.gov/sci/roofs+walls/insulation.ins_01.html
   Insulation Fact Sheet, Oak Ridge National Laboratory Building Research Program
www.naima.org
   The North American Insulation Manufacturers Association
www.cima.org
   The Cellulose Insulation Manufacturers Association

Interactions

See the following sections for information on how The Building Envelope affects other building considerations:

Chapter 4 Energy Efficiency

HEATING AND AIR CONDITIONING SYSTEMS

Heating and cooling can use over 40% of a home's energy. In cold climates, heating alone can account for as much as two thirds of a home's energy consumption. Designing, selecting, and installing more efficient, properly sized HVAC systems will keep your home buyers comfortable and happy while saving them money. Using better design and construction techniques can reduce material and installation costs while reducing the homeowner's energy bill. (Note that the efficiency of all the systems described depends on regular maintenance.) Efficient duct system design, correct register placement, duct layout, duct sealing, and insulation can account for HVAC efficiency gains of up to 30%.

Ductwork Versus No Ductwork

The type of heating and air conditioning system and equipment needed depends on whether the home has been designed with or without ductwork. If air conditioning is required, a home will need ductwork to distribute cool air. This chapter touches on ductwork design and detailing. The existence of ductwork automatically tilts the decision concerning how to heat a home in favor of warm air heating, because the cost of the system for distributing heat is already incorporated in the system for distributing cool air. However, it is possible at extra cost to add a separate heating system, either radiant baseboards or wall units, or increasingly, radiant piping in the floor. One argument in favor of a separate system is that cool air is ideally distributed near the ceiling, while heating is better delivered near floor level.

Heating System Options

Baseboard or other radiators. In climates where air conditioning is not required, baseboard radiators are a common form of heating. Attractive radiant wall panels are available, widely used in Europe, that do not interfere with furniture placement. Baseboard units can be either sheet metal or cast iron. Cast iron units, while more expensive, provide considerable mass that evens out the flow of heat and reduces short-cycling. One great advantage of radiator systems is that they are easily zoned. Zoning of heating is a green strategy because seldom-used spaces can be kept cooler, thus saving energy. The equipment used to generate heat in a radiator heating system is always a boiler or a water heater.

Radiant floor systems. Radiant floor heating using in-the-floor piping is an old technology with a history of failure due to leakage and corrosion of metal piping. With the development of "PEX" (cross-linked polyethylene) tubing, radiant floor heating has become reliably free from leakage. Its well-known comfort advantages have renewed its popularity across the country. Typically, the tubing is cast into light-weight concrete fill, to reduce the weight. However, in a passive solar heated home, it is important that the fill be normal weight to enhance its mass storage capacity (see Chapter 2, Renewable Energy, "Passive Solar Design Strategies"). It is also possible to install radiant heating under wood floors.

Radiant floor systems, like radiator systems, are easily zoned, using a central manifold. A boiler or water heater is typically used to generate heat in a radiant floor heating. In some cases, because of the low water temperature used, it is possible to use a ground-source heat pump to generate the needed warm water. However, a boiler or water heater booster will be necessary to deal with the coldest weather. Whether radiant floor heating saves energy relative to radiators or warm-air heating is controversial. What is not controversial is that radiant floor heating, properly designed, is very comfortable and highly desired by homeowners. Costs vary from $2.00/SF for systems installed as part of a planned concrete slab, up to $6.00/SF for thin-plate systems (used under wood flooring decks).

Warm air systems. While ducted warm air heating is the obvious choice for an air conditioned home, even without air conditioning it is a popular option. It is often less expensive than a hydronic system (one using warm or hot water to heat space directly) and if properly designed, can deliver excellent comfort. Poorly designed hot air systems have a bad reputation in cold climates because they are noisy and blow excessively hot air at high velocities. Good design avoids these problems. Ducted warm air systems allow easy humidification (but see concerns about excess humidity) and filtering. They also avoid the protruding baseboard or other radiators used in hydronic systems. A major advantage of warm air heating is that the system can be installed initially without air conditioning, which can easily be added later if the owner desires.

The heating equipment used with warm-air heating is typically a gas furnace, which heats the air directly. A furnace consists of a fan and filter, the combustion chamber, the heat exchanger, and if air conditioning is present, the air conditioning coil. All this equipment without the combustion chamber is called an air handler. Less commonly, heat can be generated in a furnace by electric resistance coils (often the choice in climates with very mild winters), or by burning oil.

Two other heating equipment options are available. One is a heat pump, which uses the cooling coil in an air handler to deliver heat (the equipment "runs backwards"), usually with electric resistance backup. The other option is to generate hot water with a boiler or water heater and to circulate this water through a coil in the air handler that replaces the furnace as the source of heat. This "hydro air" option is an attractive one and is discussed below.

Any ducted system is difficult to zone. If zoning is desired and the budget allows, a separate unit can be provided for each zone. Another option is to use distributed fan-coil units.

Hydro air systems. As noted previously, it is possible to use a heating coil in an air handler to create warm air for distribution through ductwork. Such a system brings with it many advantages:

- If the hot water is generated with a boiler, the same boiler can also be used to generate domestic hot water (at high efficiency).
- If the heating load is small, the water heater can produce the hot water.
- Hot water can be used simultaneously to heat air, to heat radiators, and, at a reduced temperature, to heat radiant floors.
- Water can easily be moved to remote locations in the home through piping, keeping hot elements inside the conditioned envelope of the home.

Typical hydro air systems (those that heat and cool air using water) include the following:

1. *Heating by water heater.* In climates with mild winters, hot water from the water heater can be used to heat the air for the ducted warm air heating system. A packaged coil and pump is available for this purpose. The water heater must be a high-recovery type with proper controls. A high-efficiency sealed combustion water heater is a good choice for such a system. Locate a water heater without sealed combustion outside the conditioned space, eliminating a potential source of pollution from backdrafting. Some code jurisdictions prohibit the use of the domestic water heater for space heating.

2. *Heating by boiler.* A high-efficiency boiler can be used both to feed a coil in an air handler and to heat domestic water. Instead of a water heater, a pump circulates hot water from the boiler to an insulated storage tank. Because the tank does not have a flue, it is a more efficient way to store hot water than in a typical water heater. The domestic water storage tank can be remotely located near the point of use, eliminating the water and energy loss associated with drawing hot water from a distance.

Air Conditioning System Options

A "mini-duct" system, which uses higher system pressure to move air through very small ducts, has the great advantage that ductwork can snake through smaller openings within the framing, making it easier to keep the ductwork within the conditioned envelope. Such a system is also very useful in renovations. Heating in a mini-duct system is accomplished by a hydro air coil fed by a boiler or water heater.

The ductwork found in central air conditioning systems can be zoned, but this requires motorized dampers, dump zones, and complex controls. A more reliable choice for larger and more expensive homes is to serve each area with its own individual air conditioning system. However, the best choice for most air-conditioned "green" homes is to avoid zoning. This approach reduces the possibility that underserved areas might accumulate excess amounts of humidity. In humid weather, the primary purpose of air conditioning is dehumidification, so every space needs to be served.

Evaporative Coolers

Evaporative coolers, or "swamp coolers," can be effective in dry weather but in general use large amounts of water. In humid weather, however, they are not at all effective, and they are vulnerable to the hard water that is common in dry climates. Unlike all other space conditioning systems, evaporative coolers introduce and exhaust large amounts of outside air, automatically providing extensive ventilation. If pollen is a problem, effective filtration of the incoming air is a necessity.

Sizing and Designing Systems

Use Manual J (published by the Air Conditioning Contractors of America) or other similar resources to properly size your HVAC units. Do not rely on rules of thumb, such as 600 square feet of cooled area per ton of air conditioning (A well-designed home may need only a ton for every 1,000 SF.). Oversized units perform inefficiently and can create uncomfortable conditions, especially during cooling cycles. Rather than oversizing the units, carefully design the HVAC system to be the proper size as a way of reducing callbacks. Consider natural ventilation, passive solar heating and cooling load reductions, ceiling fans, energy-efficient appliances, and other green building attributes in your calculations. Before and during construction, be sure to adjust calculations for design changes that impact heating and cooling loads (and inform HVAC subcontractors of those changes).

Heating and Air Conditioning Systems — Rules of Thumb

👍 Perform Manual J sizing calculations. Do not use rules of thumb for sizing HVAC units.
👍 Consider radiant floor heating for added comfort and efficiency.
👍 Multiple thermostats/zones may offer a cost-effective way to heat and cool larger homes.

Manual J Example*

Manual J, Load Calculation for Residential Winter and Summer Air Conditioning, is published by the Air Conditioning Contractors of America (ACCA.) The procedures in the manual calculate the building heating and cooling loads as follows:

1. Determine all dimensions of the exterior building envelope for each type of surface (wall, floor, window, door, ceiling, etc.)

2. Note R-values of all components.

3. Find the Construction Number of each component based on tables in the book.

4. Look up climatic data in the manual for the locality in which the home is being constructed.

5. Based on the Construction Number and the climatic data, find the Heat Transfer Multiplier (HTM) for the different components during the heating (Htg.) and cooling (Clg.) seasons.

6. Fill in the tables for the heating and cooling load.

7. Calculate the infiltration loads, internal gains, and latent loads in separate charts.

8. Find the grand total loads.

9. Use Manual S, Residential Equipment Selection, also published by ACCA, to help select the equipment for the home.

1	Name of Room					Entire House		
2	Running Ft. Exposed Wall						94.5	
3	Room Dimensions Ft.					32	62.5	
4	Ceiling Ht. Ft.						8	

	TYPE OF EXPOSURE		Const. No.	HTM		Area/ Length	Btuh	
				Htg.	Clg.		Htg.	Clg.
5	Gross Exposed Walls & Partitions	a b c d	12F				1,512	
6	Windows & Glass Doors Htg.	a b c d	3b	30.5		300	9,150	
7	Windows & Glass Doors Clg.	North E&W South			16 46 25	75 150 75		1,200 6,900 1,875
8	Other Doors		10D	23	10.9	42	966	458
9	Net Exposed Walls & Partitions	a b c d	12F	3.5	1.7	1,170	4,095	1,989
10	Ceilings	a b	16G	1.6	1.2	2,000	3,200	2,400
11	Floors	a b	19D	1.3	0	2,000	2,600	0
12	Infiltration HTM						11,757	5,878
13	Sub Total Btuh Loss = 6+8+9+10+11+12						31,768	20,700
14	Duct Btuh Loss			0.1			3,177	0
15	Total Btuh Loss = 13 + 14						34,945	
16	People @ 300 & Appliances= 1200							2,400
17	Sensible Btuh Gain = 7+8+9+10+11+12+16							23,100
18	Duct Btuh Gain			0.05				1,155
19	Total Sensible Gain							24,255
	Latent Gain Calculations							
	Latent Infiltration							2,471
	Latent Ventilation							0
	Latent Internal Gains							1,920
	Total Latent Gain							4,391

* A Manual J calculation takes approximately 30 to 60 minutes for an average home. The measurements for the calculations are available from the construction drawings. Manual S calculations require an additional 15 to 30 minutes.

Additional Resources

A Builder's Guide to Residential HVAC Systems, NAHB Research Center, Home Builder Press. 1997. Provides extensive information about HVAC sizing, design, and equipment selection, and also includes energy-efficiency considerations.

A Builder's Guide to Energy Efficient Homes in Georgia, Southface Energy Institute, Inc. Offers excellent descriptions and diagrams of different HVAC systems. Lots of information on sizing, installation, and duct work.

Air Conditioning Contractors of America offers *Manual J* and other information to help builders size and design their HVAC systems. www.acca.org

Web Resources

www.ashrae.org
 American Society of Heating, Refrigeration, and Air Conditioning Engineers, Inc.

www.toolbase.org/secondaryT.asp?TrackID=&CategoryID=1287&Type=
 Toolbase Services: Heating, Ventilating, and Air Conditioning

www.eere.energy.gov/buildings/homes/coolinghome.cfm
 U.S. Department of Energy: Heating and Cooling Your Home

Interactions

See the following sections for information on how Heating and Air Conditioning Systems affects other building considerations:

HEATING AND AIR CONDITIONING EQUIPMENT

Air Conditioning Equipment

A typical residential air conditioning equipment package consists of a condensing unit, placed outside the house, and an evaporator coil inside, located in the air handler or furnace. Heat pumps, natural ventilation, and other alternatives are also proven, reliable ways to cool homes in many climates.

Right-size whatever equipment is chosen for the home to save on costs and to create greater comfort (see discussion of Manual J sizing in the previous section, "Heating and Air Conditioning Systems"). Even conservatively oversized air conditioners cost more to purchase, and create humidity problems, by cycling off before they have a chance to dehumidify the air. This is uncomfortable for the homeowner and, if serious enough, may contribute to diminished indoor environmental quality. Oversized units are also poor energy performers. Include natural ventilation, shading from overhangs and landscaping, and ceiling fan effects in your calculations.

Select central air conditioning units with an ENERGY STAR® rating. ENERGY STAR® air conditioners are at least 20% more efficient than standard equipment and have a Seasonal Energy Efficiency Rating (SEER) of 12 or higher. The SEER rating is usually shown on the yellow and black EnergyGuide sticker attached to the unit's exterior.

A final consideration is noise. Some homeowners find that the noise created by a condensing unit outside can interfere with indoor or outdoor peace and quiet. Air conditioners are rated on a scale of 0 to 13 bels (a bel is 10 decibels). Most air conditioners and heat pumps operate in the range of 8 to 9 bels, although some units are as quiet as 6.8 bels. Units with variable speed fans are among the quietest (see below). Noise can also be transmitted directly through the electrical conduit and tubing to the house wall from a condenser placed close to the house.

Variable Speed Units

Units with multi-speed compressors and with variable speed indoor fans are more efficient than conventional units. They can achieve SEER ratings of up to 17, but at a higher cost than standard units. Added advantages include quieter operation and better dehumidification.

Heat Pumps

Heat pumps both heat and cool homes. See the following "Heating Equipment" section for more tips on heat pumps.

Heating Equipment

Residential boiler or furnace efficiency is measured by annual fuel utilization efficiency (AFUE). AFUE is a measure of how efficiently the appliance is using electricity or fossil fuels (oil or gas) over the course of a typical year. Although condensing units cost more than noncondensing units, selecting a condensing fossil-fueled furnace or boiler may be a good choice in areas with high heating costs. The AFUE of conventional equipment is limited to approximately 80%. Above this efficiency, flue gasses condense and corrode the equipment. Once this limit is breached with condensing appliances, they are typically designed for 90-95% AFUE. Vents are typically 2" PVC piping, exiting through the sidewall, and the units draw in their own combustion air through another PVC pipe (they are "sealed combustion" appliances). There may be restrictions regarding the proximity of vents to door and window openings, the length of run, and the number of bends. See the "Combustion Safety" section in Chapter 6, Indoor Environmental Quality, for more information on how to mitigate indoor air hazards (such as backdrafting) through proper design and installation of combustion appliances.

If electricity is the only fuel source for heating, a heat pump (air or ground-source) system or zoned electric resistance system should be considered. Central electric furnaces or boilers will be expensive to operate, unless the heating season is brief. Heat pumps are more efficient. Zoned electric baseboards or wall heaters (with their own thermostats) allow you to provide heat only when and where it is desired. There are minimal distribution system losses. Conventional programmable thermostats are not compatible with heat pumps; use special programmable thermostats designed specifically for heat pumps.

Geothermal Heat Pumps

Also called ground source heat pumps, geothermal units heat and cool the home by using the constant temperature of the earth as a source of heat in the winter and as a heat sink during the summer. The performance of geothermal heat pumps is typically better than air-source heat pumps, with Coefficients of Performance (COP) typically in the range of 3.5 to 4.5. These values translate into SEER ratings of 12 to 15. Select units with an ENERGY STAR® label. Note that some units may use the Heating Season Performance Factor (HSPF) rather than COP. Select a unit with an HSPF rating of 7.5 or higher. Other advantages include their long life expectancy (25 years) and their ability to deliver hot water at a greater efficiency than standard electric water heaters. Disadvantages include higher first costs ($1,000 to $1,500 per ton higher than conventional HVAC) and land requirements for horizontal buried pipes for heat transfer (ground source). To mitigate land requirements, consider vertical loops. The Geothermal Heat Pump Consortium promotes geothermal heat pumps to builders and home buyers, sometimes with financial incentives.

Air Source Heat Pumps

These are the most common type of heat pumps and, like the geothermal units, both heat and cool the home. Most heat pumps operate at least twice as effectively as conventional electric resistance heating systems. Air-source heat pumps should have an outdoor thermostat to prevent operation of electrical strip heaters when temperatures climb above 35 or 40 degrees. Some heat pumps are installed with duel-fuel or piggyback systems that heat the home with gas when temperatures drop to the point where the heat pump can no longer meet the heating load of the home, typically below 25 to 35 degrees. Select units with an HSPF of 7 or greater, as these meet ENERGY STAR® requirements.

Efficient Duct Design and Installation

Duct leakage constitutes 10% to 30% of heating and cooling loads in many homes. In addition, duct leakage can lessen comfort and endanger health and safety. Make sure your HVAC contractor is, at a minimum, familiar with the design information, products, and installation techniques described below.

The three most common types of duct material used in home construction are metal, fiber glass duct board, and flex-duct. Duct work should be insulated if not inside the conditioned space. If the ducts are inside the conditioned space, duct liner helps attenuate sound from the HVAC unit and between rooms. Both metal and fiber glass duct board are rigid and installed in pieces. Many contractors use an all-6-inch system. Proper duct size depends on the estimated heating and cooling load for each room in the house, the length, type and shape of the duct, and the operating characteristics of the HVAC system, such as the pressure, temperature, and fan speed. Use *Manual D, Duct Design* published by the Air Conditioning Contractors of America (ACCA) to calculate the proper air flow and duct size for each room. Duct systems made with fiber glass duct board provide the advantage of being insulated and having low air leakage, two features that save energy.

Efficient Duct Design and Installation Diagrams

Disconnected Ducts Are High Priorities

Ducts can become disconnected during initial installation, maintenance, or even normal operation. They should be checked periodically for problems.

Duct Leaks in Inside Spaces

Although this supply duct is theoretically in conditioned space, the supply leaks pressurize the band joist area and air leaks to the outside. The best solution—seal all duct leaks and all building envelope air leaks

Disconnection at boot

Figure 8-4
Seal All Leaks in Air Handling Unit

Sometimes, disconnected ducts can be hidden behind the insulation. Look for kinks or curves where there is no elbow.

Many air handling cabinets come from the factory with leaks, which should be sealed with duct-sealing mastic. Removable panels should be sealed with tape.

Removable panel sealed   Mastic
with tape

Efficient Duct Design and Installation Diagrams (continued)

Shelf-Mounted Systems Without Returns

Non-ducted returns can severely depressurize mechanical room closets, not only sapping the system's efficiency, but also creating ideal conditions for backdrafting and other air quality problems. Seal all leaks with mastic or caulk.

The return should be connected to the home via a well sealed duct. All holes from the mechanical room closet to other spaces should be completely sealed.

Seal All Leaky Takeoffs

Apply mastic

Leaky return takeoff pulls in surrounding air

Seal leaky filter rack with rated aluminum tape

Figure 8-7
Sealing Leaky Boots

Mastic

Use mastic to completely seal all leaky seams and holes. Use mesh tape with mastic to cover cracks over 1/8-inch wide.

Duct Installation Tips: High-Priority Leaks

High-priority leaks include the following:

1. Disconnected components, including take-offs that are not fully inserted, plenums or ducts that have been dislodged, tears in flex-duct, and strained connections between ductwork (visible when the duct bends where there is no elbow)
2. The joints between sections of branch ductwork
3. The return take-offs, elbows, boots, and other connections (if the return is built into an interior wall, all connections and seams must be carefully sealed)
4. The take-offs from the main supply plenum or trunk line
5. Any framing in the building used as ductwork, such as a "panned" joist where sheet metal nailed to floor joists provides a space for conditioned air to flow (it is preferable to avoid using framing as a part of the duct system)

In addition, pay careful attention to the connections between the air handling unit and the supply and return plenums. Check all of the seams in the air handling unit, plenums, and rectangular ductwork—particularly underneath components and in any other tight areas. Also seal the holes for the refrigerant, thermostat, and condensate lines. Use tape rather than mastic to seal the seams in the panel of the air handling unit so they can be removed during servicing. After completion of service and maintenance work, such as filter changing, advise the homeowner to make sure the seams are retaped. Lastly, check the connections near the supply registers: between the branch ductwork and the boot, the seams of the elbows, and all other potential leaks in these areas.

Duct Installation Tips: Low-Priority Leaks

Low-priority leaks include the following:

1. Longitudinal seams in round metal ductwork
2. The boot and the register

Additional Duct Design and Installation Recommendations

1. Use only high-quality caulking or foam sealant and duct-sealing water-based mastic with fiber glass mesh (highly preferred). This strategy may add $20 to $55 and one person day to the cost of a $5,000 system, but it will reap energy and dollar savings for the owner.

2. *Never* use unrated duct tape. Tapes that are rated as UL-181 have been tested and will maintain their sealing properties over the life of the home.

3. In energy-efficient houses (homes with extra insulation and high-performance windows) it is not necessary to place registers on the outside walls or under or above windows to maintain occupant comfort, as is traditional practice. Locating both supply and return ducts near the core of the house saves builders labor and material costs.

4. Locate ducts within the conditioned space to minimize leakage problems.

5. Use duct insulation of at least R-6 value, and install the vapor retarder to the outside of the insulation facing away from the duct.

6. Round and rectangular metal ducts must be sealed with mastic and insulated during installation. It is important to seal the seams first, because insulation does not stop air leaks.

7. Flex-duct has higher pressure losses than those associated with metal duct work. Flex-duct is flexible and comes in long sections. If flex-duct is used, it is important that the soft lining material of the flex-duct not be punctured or torn and that the layout be carefully designed to minimize pressure losses.

8. Minimize use of elbows and sharp turns.

9. Locate registers so that they do not blow air directly onto occupants. This is particularly important when using heat pumps or other moderate temperature heating sources.

10. Locate intake ducts away from exhausts from the laundry, kitchen, chimney, or fireplace.

11. The air-tightness of duct work can be tested after installation using calibrated fans and testing procedures similar to blower door tests.

HVAC Controls: Programmable Thermostats

Programmable thermostats are an inexpensive way for builders to help home buyers increase the comfort and energy efficiency of their homes. Typical costs are $40 to $60 per unit, while savings of 6% to 10% may be realized in the home's heating and cooling costs. Programmable thermostats work with most types of central HVAC systems, but there are special programmable heat pump thermostats, so do not use conventional models with heat pumps. Like nonprogrammable thermostats, they should be located out of direct sunlight and away from heat-producing appliances, registers, and other sources of heating and cooling. A good spot is 4 to 5 feet above the floor in an interior hallway or near an air return.

Air Conditioning Equipment — Rules of Thumb

👍 Correctly size the unit for its intended application. Save costs by not oversizing. Oversizing results in humidity problems and poor energy performance.

👍 Select units with the ENERGY STAR® label.

👍 Shade outdoor units with trees, shrubs, and other landscaping, while being careful not to block airflow to the unit.

👍 Consider units with a multi-speed compressor and/or blower.

👍 Select quiet operating units.

👍 Consider more efficient geothermal heat pumps to meet both heating and cooling loads.

Heating Equipment — Rules of Thumb

👍 In cold climates, select heating equipment with an AFUE rating of 90% or greater.

👍 Select heat pumps and other equipment with the ENERGY STAR® label.

👍 In moderate and warm climates, consider air-source and geothermal heat pumps for both heating and cooling loads.

👍 Size the heating system appropriately. Save material costs by not oversizing.

👍 Connect the heating system to programmable thermostats.

Additional Resources

A Builder's Guide to Residential HVAC Systems, NAHB Research Center, Home Builder Press. 1997. Provides extensive information about HVAC sizing, design, and equipment selection, and also includes energy-efficiency considerations.

Consumers' Guide to Certified Efficiency Ratings for Residential Heating and Water Heating Equipment, Gas Appliance Manufacturers Association, Arlington, Virginia. This directory lists the efficiency ratings of all models of gas furnaces, boilers, and water heaters according to manufacturer.

A Builder's Guide to Energy Efficient Homes in Georgia, Southface Energy Institute, Inc. Offers excellent descriptions and diagrams of different HVAC systems. Lots of information on sizing, installation, and duct work.

U.S. Department of Energy Office of Building Technology, State and Community Programs offers a comprehensive set of information on all forms of building technology, including HVAC systems. www.eere.energy.gov/buildings

Web Resources

www.ashrae.org
   American Society of Heating, Refrigeration, and Air Conditioning
   Engineers, Inc.
www.toolbase.org/secondaryT.asp?TrackID=&CategoryID=1287&Type=
   Toolbase Services: Heating, Ventilating, and Air Conditioning
www.builtgreen.org/articles/0308_HVAC_sizing.htm
   Built Green Colorado: HVAC Equipment Sizing Calcs

Interactions

See the following sections for information on how Heating and Air
Conditioning Equipment affects other building considerations:

WATER HEATING

Water heating is the second largest energy use in new homes after space conditioning (heating and cooling). The five areas where improvement is possible are:

- More efficient hot water generation
- Reduced storage (or standby) losses in hot water equipment
- Reduced piping losses
- Reduction in hot water temperatures to provide the minimum acceptable temperature for intended use
- Reduced end use

Water Heater Efficiency

Water heater efficiency is described by the Energy Factor (EF) rating. The EF takes into account the over-all efficiency at which the fuel (gas, electricity, or oil) is converted to useful water heating energy, including standby losses.

In all cases, a higher EF indicates a higher efficiency. However, electric water heater EFs should not be compared to gas. Often, the additional cost of a high-efficiency unit is quite low compared to the savings that can be achieved. Higher efficiencies are realized through increased tank insulation and, for gas- and oil-fired heaters, through improved heat transfer from the flame to the water.

Gas-fired water heaters generally cost $150 to $200 more than electric water heaters of similar construction and warranty. Yet gas water heaters typically cost *less* to operate in comparison to electric water heaters. Consider more than just equipment cost when choosing which fuel to use for water heating (Chapter 2, Renewable Energy, "Solar Water Heating Systems"). Local utilities may offer electricity generated by 100% renewable sources.

If a gas water heater is chosen, consider a direct-vented condensing unit or power-vented unit. Condensing units are expensive (usually around $2,000). They have EFs of approximately 0.85, however, and generally have large enough capacity to provide space heating via radiant floors or hydronic coil.

Insulate Hot Water Tank and Lines

Reduce piping and standby losses—losses that can account for more than 30% of water heating energy—by wrapping the storage tank and insulating pipes. Wrap storage tanks with R-16 insulation jackets, being careful not to cover the relief or drain valve or the air inlet to the gas or oil burner. Insulate hot water pipes from the heater to their end use with R-6.

Insulating Jackets for Electric and Gas Water Heaters

Hot   Cold

Heat traps reduce heat loss

Hot   Cold

Insulate first four feet of all metal pipes extending out of water heater

Electric Water Heater.   Gas Water Heater

Be sure to insulate all hot water pipes in unconditioned space and the first 6 feet extending out of the water heater. Water jackets and insulation are inexpensive, easy to install, and readily available. Water jackets start at $10. Heat traps and anti-convection valves also reduce heat losses.

Reducing Losses at Remote Fixtures

There are several strategies for reducing water use and water heating losses that occur when hot water is drawn from a fixture that is distant from the water heater:

- Locate the water heater or water storage tank in close proximity to the bathroom, washing machine, and kitchen.
- Consider point-of-use, instantaneous water heating systems.
- Use energy-efficient, on-demand recirculating systems.
- Use a manifold PEX water supply tubing system in which 3/8" diameter "home runs" are run directly from the water heater to the fixtures.

Set Water Heater to 120 Degrees

Set water heater temperature to 120 degrees. Higher temperatures lead to scalding and more standby losses, while lower temperatures can lead to Legionella bacteria in the water tank. If higher temperatures are desired for washing dishes, use dishwashers with booster heaters.

Alternative Water Heating Systems

Consider water heating options such as solar water heating, heat pump water heaters, heat recovery processes, and combination space and water heating systems. These systems and options can significantly improve efficiency over traditional hot water tank systems.

Instantaneous water heaters only heat water as it is called for and do not require significant amounts of storage. This means they have minimal stand-by losses. Point-of-use instantaneous water heaters heat water at each individual end use rather than in a central location.

Water Heating — Rules of Thumb

👍 Locate the water heater as close as possible to the bathroom, kitchen, and washing machine in order to reduce heat losses.

👍 Size correctly to meet demand and use the smallest water heater possible. Smaller water heaters are typically more efficient because they have lower standby losses.

👍 Install heat traps to reduce convective heat loss from the tank.

👍 Insulate hot water tanks with R-16 jackets without covering the relief or drain valve or the air inlet to the gas or oil burner.

👍 Insulate hot water pipes from the heater to the end use with R-6 insulation. If this level of insulation is prohibitive, insulate all hot water pipes in unconditioned space and the first 6 feet extending out from the water heater.

👍 Set water heater temperature to 120 degrees. If higher temperatures are desired for dish washing, select dishwashers with booster heaters.

Additional Resources

Builder's Guide to Energy Efficient Homes, Southface Energy Institute, Inc. September 1999. Good general information. See p. 117 for Heat Recovery Units/Desuperheaters.

The Consumers' Directory of Certified Efficiency Ratings, Gas Appliance Manufacturers Association (GAMA). Provides a concise listing of Energy Factors for water heaters of all fuel types. www.gamanet.org

Web Resources

www.toolbase.org/secondaryT.asp?TrackID=&CategoryID=1318
  Toolbase Services: Water Heaters
www.eere.energy.gov/erec/factsheets/eewtrhr.html
  U.S. Department of Energy, Energy Efficiency and Renewable Energy: Energy Efficient Water Heating

Interactions

See the following sections for information on how Water Heating affects other building considerations:

LIGHTING

Standard incandescent bulbs are the most common but also the most inefficient lighting sources for homes. The lighting industry has produced a number of alternative lighting systems. When designing a lighting plan, consult with knowledgeable professionals about optimum lighting levels and different types of fixtures and lamps. In addition to the purchase price, consider the long-term energy costs of fixtures before choosing any particular one. Energy-efficient lighting produces less heat, thereby saving money on cooling as well as lighting costs.

Energy-efficient lighting should be placed in areas of high continuous use such as the kitchen, sitting areas, and outside the home. Use task or accent lighting for specific areas where greater illumination is desired, rather than over-illuminating the entire room. Daylight from windows, lightpipes, and other glazing should be maximized without incurring an energy penalty of unwanted heat gain or loss. Motion sensors, photo sensors, and timers should be part of the exterior lighting design.

This section discusses the following alternatives to incandescent lighting:

- Daylight
- Compact and other fluorescent lighting for indoor use
- Sealed IC recessed lighting
- Outdoor lighting
- Occupant and photo sensors, dimmers, and other controls

Daylight

Bringing in natural light is the ideal way to increase comfort and aesthetics in a home while reducing energy consumption. Common examples include light tubes or light pipes, skylights, and clerestory windows. Careful consideration should be given to skylights and windows to avoid unwanted heat gains and losses (see Chapter 2, Renewable Energy, "Passive Solar Design"). Light pipes provide natural light for the home's interior or in areas where other issues, such as privacy in a bathroom, restrict the use of traditional glazing. Light pipes can also protect the home from unwanted heat gains and losses associated with traditional windows. Light pipes typically range in cost from $200 to $500. Light tubes and skylights must be well sealed to prevent air infiltration or water leakage.

Compact and Other Fluorescent Lighting for Indoor Use

Fluorescent lighting has improved dramatically. Fluorescent fixtures that use electronic ballasts do not flicker or hum. Select bulbs with a high color rendition index (80 or higher), sometimes referred to as CRI. These emit high-quality light that is close to incandescent lighting. Compact fluorescent bulbs easily fit in recessed, wall, or ceiling mounted fixtures, and many models can be used with dimmers. Fluorescent lights last as much as 10 times longer than incandescent bulbs and reduce energy use by 50% to 70%, although they are more expensive than incandescent bulbs. Compact and other fluorescent bulbs are widely available in a range of wattages and bulb sizes.

Fluorescent Lighting Guidelines		
Type of Room	Size of Room	Amount of Light Needed (Watts)
Living Room, Bedroom,	under 150 sf	40–60
Family Room, or	150–250 sf	60–80
Recreation Room	over 250 sf	.33 Watts/sf
Kitchen,	75 sf	55–70
Laundry, or	75–120 sf	60–80
Workshop	over 120 sf	.75 Watts/sf

Recessed Lighting

Fixtures should not penetrate into any insulated area. According to Austin-based architect Peter Pfeiffer, "They tend to let a lot of heat out in the winter and humidity in the summer, even the so-called airtight ones." They are especially problematic in cathedral ceilings. In cold climates, if they are near the eaves, they leak heat into the attic space and can contribute to ice dams.

Outdoor Lighting

Metal halide and compact fluorescent are the most energy-efficient choices for outdoor lighting. Use motion detectors to control outdoor lighting. Motion detectors cost approximately $30. The detectors will ensure the lights are on for safety and security purposes when needed and off at all other times.

Solar powered lights that charge during the day are a good option for lighting pathways and driveways. They typically cost $30 to $50 per fixture.

Outdoor lighting should be pointed down toward the ground or home exterior to prevent unnecessary nighttime light pollution.

Occupant and Photo Sensors, Dimmers, and Other Controls

Consider using solid-state dimmers and multilevel switches for indoor lighting. Dimmers are a popular lighting control for indoor lights and are compatible with almost all types of lighting, including many fluorescent lamps, such as compact models. Occupancy and photo sensors are primarily used for outdoor lighting, although they can be used inside the home in seldom-used spaces or areas that are daylit or use electric lights.

Energy-Efficient Lighting — Rules of Thumb

👍 Increase the amount of natural light in a home and reduce energy costs.

👍 Consider using light pipes to bring natural light into the interior of homes.

👍 Compact and other fluorescent lighting should be used as much as possible, particularly in the kitchen, sitting areas, and outside.

👍 Select fluorescent fixtures with electronic ballasts to eliminate noise and flicker.

👍 Avoid recessed lighting in insulated ceilings.

👍 Use motion detectors or occupancy sensors to control outdoor lighting.

👍 Use metal halide or fluorescent fixtures for outdoor lighting.

👍 Use solid-state dimmers and multilevel switches that allow for variable lighting levels.

Additional Resources

Illuminating Engineering Society of North America (IESNA) publishes helpful information on lighting products, including controls. www.iesna.org; 800-862-2086

Sustainable Building Technical Manual: Green Building Design, Construction, and Operations, Public Technology, Inc., U.S. Green Building Council, U.S. Department of Energy, and U.S. Environmental Protection Agency. 1996. Chapter 9. PTI, 1301 Pennsylvania Ave. NW, Washington, D.C., 20004-1793. 800-852-4934; pti.nw.dc.us

A Builder's Guide to Energy Efficient Homes in Georgia, Georgia Environmental Facilities Authority, Division of Energy Resources. September 1999. p. 124–125. Southface Energy Institute, Inc., 241 Pine Street, Atlanta, GA 30308. 404-872-3549; www.southface.org

Lighting Research Center. 21 Union Street, Troy, NY 12180-3352. 518-687-7100; www.lrc.rpi.edu

Web Resources

www.eere.energy.gov/erec/factsheets/eelight.html
U.S. Department of Energy, Energy Efficiency and Renewable Energy: Energy Efficient Lighting

www.energystar.gov/index.cfm?c=lighting.pr_lighting
U.S. Department of Energy, Energy Star: Change a Light, Change the World

www.toolbase.org
Toolbase Services

www.wbdg.org/design/resource.php?cn=0&rp=15
Whole Building Design Guide: Energy Efficient Lighting

Interactions

See the following sections for information on how Lighting affects other building considerations:

APPLIANCES

A builder's influence regarding which appliances are purchased for a home varies from complete control to none at all. Regardless of who is procuring them, appliances are often overlooked as a means of improving energy efficiency in homes. Appliances consume nearly one fifth of a home's energy, with the refrigerator commanding a 9% share. Use "Energy-Efficient Appliances – Rules of Thumb" as a checklist for your appliance decisions.

Typical Energy Costs for Appliances			
Appliance	Average Model ($/yr)	High Efficiency Model ($/yr)	10-Year Savings
Refrigerator (manual defrost)	56	36	$200
Refrigerator/freezer (frost free)	96	56	$400
Freezer (frost free)	108	60	$480
Electric range	48	40	$80
Gas range	36	28	$80
Electric clothes dryer	56	44	$120
Gas clothes dryer	24	20	$40
Dishwasher*	56	36	$200
Color television	20	8	$120
Lighting	60	28	$320

* Includes cost of water heating. Source: Adapted from "Saving Energy and Money with Home Appliances," by the Massachusetts Audubon Society and the American Council for an Energy Efficient Economy

Buy ENERGY STAR® Appliances

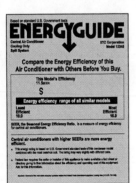

In general, builders should select cost-effective, energy-efficient models with the ENERGY STAR® label. ENERGY STAR® is a government-sponsored program that identifies products that are significantly more energy efficient than the minimum government standards. The amount by which an appliance must exceed the minimum standards varies for each type of product. ENERGY STAR® labels can be found on almost all major appliances. Selecting products with the ENERGY STAR® label can be an effective and easy way to market your home as a cost-effective and energy-efficient house.

Money Isn't All You're Saving

When buying ENERGY STAR® appliances is not possible, builders should select appliances that are rated among the more efficient in their class by the yellow EnergyGuide label. At this time, EnergyGuide labels are not required on all types of appliances. These labels compare how much it will cost to operate one appliance per year, in comparison to competing models with the highest and lowest annual energy costs. Check with your state energy office as well as your utility company to see if there are incentives or rebate programs that support installation of energy-efficient appliances in your homes.

Refrigerators/Freezers

Refrigerators/freezers are big energy users because they operate 24 hours a day, 365 days a year. Efficient models can cost half as much to operate as inefficient ones. ENERGY STAR® refrigerators are at least 10% more efficient than the minimum standards effective as of July 2001. In general, most of the energy-efficient models are in the 16 to 20 cubic foot range. Side-by-side refrigerators, automatic ice dispensers, and through-the-door water dispensers are popular options that, unfortunately, decrease a model's efficiency and therefore increase operating costs. When designing the kitchen, locate the refrigerator away from heat sources such as ovens, ranges, dishwashers, forced air vents or radiators, and direct sunlight. Also be sure to provide adequate ventilation around the refrigerator. Without adequate ventilation, the compressor works harder because the heat expelled by the coils cannot escape.

Dishwashers

Water heating accounts for 80% of the energy consumed by a dishwasher. In general, models that use less water use less energy. As of January 2001, ENERGY STAR® dishwasher models use at least 25% less energy than is called for by government standards (the old specification was 13%). Builders should select models that include the following characteristics:

- An Energy Factor of 0.58 or higher
- Light, medium, and heavy wash settings
- Energy saving "no-heat dry" or "air-dry" switch
- Booster or supplemental water heater that allows the water heater to be set to 120 degrees

Dishwasher Cost-Effectiveness Example		
Performance	**Base Model[a]**	**Recommended Level**
Energy Factor	0.46	0.58
Annual Energy Use	700 kWh	555 kWh
With Electric Water Heating		
Annual Energy Cost	$42	$33
Lifetime Energy Cost	$400	$320
Lifetime Energy Savings	–	**$80**
With Gas Water Heating		
Annual Energy Cost	$21	$16
Lifetime Energy Cost	$220	$170
Lifetime Energy Savings	–	**$50**

[a] The efficiency (Energy Factor) of the Base Model is just sufficient to meet current U.S. DOE national appliance standards.

Dishwashers range in price from $300 to $1,000. Builders may market energy- and water-efficient dishwashers from several additional perspectives, including quiet operation, performance, ease of use, and reliability.

Ovens, Stoves, and Ranges

Convection ovens are 33% more efficient than standard ovens. Gas ovens and stoves are typically less expensive to operate but are more expensive to purchase. Electronic cooktops with ceramic glass covers are more efficient than coil or disk electric stoves. Induction elements that use electromagnetic energy to heat the pan are the most efficient.

Clothes Washers

Water heating can account for 90% of a clothes washer's energy use. ENERGY STAR® washers, which come in top-loading and front-loading models, use 30% to 40% less energy than conventional washers. Front-loading models, which are also called tumble washers or horizontal axis machines, typically get clothes cleaner and are gentler on clothes than traditional top loading machines. They are the most energy-efficient models, with average energy savings of 60%, although more efficient, advanced-design top-loaders are available. Front-loading machines also use 36% less water than traditional washers, and some spin clothes faster, which dries clothes better and reduces time in the drier. Depending on the amount and manner of use, as well as water, electricity, and gas rates, front-loading machines can save consumers $100 or more during each year of the machine's 13-15 year lifespan. These savings far exceed the $200 to $300 additional purchase cost. Builders should select washers that offer several wash and rinse cycle (temperature) options as well as several sizes of loads. Front loaders also tend to be more reliable, because they do not have an agitator (the part that most often fails on washers).

Clothes Dryers

Like most appliances, clothes dryers can be gas or electric. Where natural gas is available, gas dryers have historically been less expensive to operate but have a higher first cost. Electric dryers are just the opposite: more expensive to operate with a lower first cost. Builders should select models that detect "dryness" and then shut off automatically, or those that offer energy-saving settings. Some dryers have moisture sensors that typically save from 10% to 15% over standard driers. Over time, these models save a considerable amount of energy.

Energy-Efficient Appliances — Rules of Thumb

👍 Buy and install ENERGY STAR® rated appliances. Alternatively, select appliances that are rated among the most efficient in their class as indicated on the EnergyGuide label.

👍 Allow for adequate ventilation areas around the refrigerator.

👍 Electronic cooktops with ceramic glass covers are more efficient than disk or coil stoves.

👍 Use quietness, performance, and other non-energy factors to support your selection of energy-efficient dishwashers and clothes washers.

👍 Some front-loading clothes washers also help dry clothes better than top-loading models, allowing for energy savings during the dry cycle.

👍 Consider clothes dryers with moisture and temperature sensors.

👍 Gas appliances are typically less expensive to operate but have a higher first cost.

👍 Check with your local utility and state energy office for rebates and other incentives that may be awarded for installing energy-efficient appliances.

Additional Resources

Consumers Union publishes *Consumer Reports* magazine and the *Consumer Reports Annual Buying Guide,* which rate appliances for reliability, convenience, and efficiency. 800-500-9760; www.consumerreports.org

Home Energy magazine provides energy conservation tips as well as an archive of energy consumption data of old refrigerators. 510-524-5405; www.homeenergy.org/homeenergy.html

American Council for an Energy Efficient Economy (ACEEE) publishes the *Consumer Guide to Home Energy Savings.* 202-429-0063; www.aceee.org

Consortium for Energy Efficiency (CEE) provides information on energy-efficient clothes washers. 617-589-3949; www.cee1.org

DOE and EPA have appliance model listing as part of their ENERGY STAR® program. 800-363-3732; www.energystar.gov

E Source Technology Atlas Series Volume 5 Residential Appliances provides information on appliance specifications and efficiency standards. 720-548-5000; www.esource.com/public/products/prosp_atlas.asp

Web Resources

www.toolbase.org/secondaryT.asp?TrackID=&CategoryID=1280&Type=
Toolbase Services: Appliances

www.aceee.org/consumerguide/mostenef.htm
American Council for an Energy-Efficient Economy: The Most Energy-Efficient Appliances

www.eere.energy.gov/EE/buildings_appliances.html
U.S. Department of Energy: Appliances

www.energystar.gov/index.cfm?c=appliances.pr_appliances
ENERGY STAR: Appliances

http://Yosemite1.epa.gov/estar/homes.nsf/homepage?openform
    U.S. EPA: ENERGY STAR for New Homes
www.homeenergy.gov
    Home Energy Magazine

Interactions

See the following sections for information on how Appliances affects other building considerations:

Chapter 5   Efficient Water Use

INDOOR WATER USE

Since 1900, per capita water use in the United States has quadrupled. Americans now consume an average of over 100 gallons per person per day for indoor and outdoor uses. For homes on public water and sewage systems, water efficiency can be an important community issue. Just about every gallon of water that your local government purifies to meet consumption needs must also be treated after it is used. In this way, two environmental issues, protecting the supply of fresh water and the treatment of wastewater, can be solved through water efficiency.

The table below presents average indoor water consumption data for an American home. The American Water Works Association estimates that indoor water consumption can be reduced by 32% to a total of 49.6 gallons per person per day by installing readily available water-efficient fixtures and appliances and by minimizing leaks.

According to Sandia National Laboratory's estimate, 80% of the cost of delivering water can be directly attributed to energy requirements for pumping, processing, or treating the water. Considering the average cost of domestic water in the U.S. is about $2.50/1000 gallons, the total energy cost associated with providing residential water in our country is $20 billion per year. That's about 3% of our country's $700 billion energy bill. To solve this problem in the short term, conservation of water must become a top priority in this country. With 97% of the world's water in our oceans and only three-tenths of one percent of the world's water being potable, our next goal must be to focus on non-polluting, desalination strategies . . . derived from solar energy.

—Mike Nicklas, "Chair's Corner,"
Solar Today, Sept/Oct 2003

Typical Indoor Household Water Use (1999)		
Type of Use	Daily Use (gallons per person)	Approximate % of Total Indoor Use
Toilets	20.1	27.7
Clothes Washers	15.1	20.9
Showers	12.6	17.3
Faucets	11.1	15.3
Leaks	10.0	13.8
Other	1.5	2.1
Baths	1.2	1.6
Dishwashers	1.0	1.3
Total	**72.6**	**100.0**

Source: Water Miser, 1999 American Water Works.

Note: This table does not include residential water use *outside* the home, which brings the typical total to about 105 gallons per person per day. Typical residential water consumption for lawns, gardens, and car washing is highly variable across the country, ranging between 25 and 200 gallons per person per day.

Low-Flow Toilets

Federal law (Energy Policy Act of 1992) requires 1.6 gallons per flush (gpf) toilets for all new construction. Because quality can vary greatly, it is important to research and carefully select toilets, showerheads, and faucets. Some of the first low-flow toilets did not perform adequately. Recently, manufacturers have produced much-improved low-flow toilets that work well and are affordable. Builders may also want to consider using dual-flush low-flow toilets and composting toilets where codes permit.

Low-Flow Faucets

The Energy Policy Act of 1992 limits faucet and showerhead water use to 2.5 gallons per minute (gpm) at 80 psi. Builders should specify faucets with a 2.2 gpm rating or less. Aerators placed on faucets add air to the water stream, thus boosting the effectiveness of the flow and reducing water consumption. Flow-restrictors are not recommended in areas with low water pressure.

Low-Flow Showerheads

Superior-performing low-flow showerheads with flow rates between 1.5 and 2.0 gpm are available. Homeowner complaints regarding low-flow showerheads are most often associated with their "feel" and eventual clogging. Be wary of atomizer and aerator showerheads that deliver water in fine droplets to save water. (Aerators are recommended for faucets but not for showerheads; the cooling effect is so great with these types of heads that users feel their shower is of poor quality.) Avoid flow-restrictor showerheads in areas with low water pressure. Instead, look for showerheads with flow rates less than 2.5 gpm that have the feel of higher flow and are guaranteed against clogging. These are commonly available at an added cost of approximately $10 per head. Not all showerheads have the same flow rate; research the available brands and models and select carefully. Some showerheads also use temporary cut-off valves that attach to or are incorporated into the showerhead. They stop the water flow when the individual is soaping or shampooing. When the water flow is reactivated, it emerges at the same temperature, eliminating the need to remix the hot and cold water.

Appliances and Recirculating Systems

See "Appliances" in Chapter 4, Energy Efficiency, for information on dishwashers and clothes washers. Some builders may also wish to consider hot water recirculating systems. These systems are best employed in homes with faucets distant from the hot water heater. Several types are available for as little as $350. Water savings are achieved when homeowners no longer run a faucet for minutes before hot water arrives. Energy savings are also realized.

Leaks

Leaks are insidious and costly, averaging 10% of a home's water consumption. Prevention is the key. Use quality pipes, fittings, valves, and other hardware (see "Plumbing Hardware/NSF Cerfitication" below). In addition, carefully inspect the work of plumbing subcontractors. Once the plumbing system is complete, the American Water Works Association suggests an easy "zero-read" test to check for leaks. Check the water meter during a period when no water is being used. Do this by reading the last two right hand digits or dials. Wait 30 minutes (the longer the better as some leaks are cyclical) and then take another reading. If usage has occurred, first check the flapper valve and overflow level in all toilets. If no problems are detected there, pipelines or an in-ground irrigation system may be likely sources of the leak(s). Be sure to pass on the zero-read test to your home buyers so they can continue to check for leaks on an annual basis.

Plumbing Hardware / NSF Certification

NSF International, The Public Health and Safety Company™, is a nonprofit, nongovernmental organization. NSF International is a leader in standards development, product certification, education, and risk management for public health and safety.

Select NSF-approved plumbing fixtures and fittings that are of top quality in terms of water conservation and leak resistance. Obtain proof of NSF certification for each plumbing component. The NSF mark on plastic plumbing products and materials confirms that NSF has assessed and certified a product's conformity with NSF Standard 14 requirements for its intended end use. Plastic piping products designed for potable water applications must also meet the health effects requirements of ANSI/NSF 61, which ensure that any impurities imparted indirectly from a product into the drinking water are within acceptable levels.

Potable Water Quality

To ensure adequate water quality, upon completion of the plumbing system, flush the system and conduct water sampling at taps and service lines entering the home. At a minimum, test for lead, copper, pH, arsenic, and turbidity. Water quality results should be within EPA maximum contaminant levels and action levels (EPA 40 Code of Federal Regulations, Parts 141-149). To achieve the highest quality water for cooking and drinking, consider installing filters at taps and/or at the service line(s) or house main. Some filter systems may require periodic filter replacement, addition of chemicals, and, owing to back wash requirements, increased water use.

Efficient Interior Water Use — Rules of Thumb

👍 Low-flow toilets may significantly reduce the total number of gallons used in a typical home. Some models perform significantly better than others; research and carefully select 1.6 gpf toilets.

👍 Install low-flow, non-clogging showerheads (1.5 to 2.0 gpm) and faucets (less than 2.2 gpm).

👍 Minimize leaks by educating home buyers about plumbing maintenance (this also prevents call-backs and owner dissatisfaction). Use the zero-read method to test for leaks.

👍 Ensure plumbing integrity during construction by inspection and by using NSF-certified components that meet ANSI/NSF 61 and NSF Standard 14.

👍 Flush newly installed plumbing systems and conduct water samplings at service lines.

Additional Resources

Vickers, Amy, *Handbook of Water Use and Conservation*, Lewis Publishers/CRS Press. 1999.

Liebold, Warren, "Water Efficiency, Shopping for a Good Toilet or Showerhead." An article and opinion survey covering various brands of water efficient toilets and showerheads. home.earthlink.net/~wliebold

"An Energy-Saving Product That's Actually Convenient?", *Energy Design Update*. July 1997, p. 8. This article reviews one hot water recirculating system.

The Water Smart Home Program, Greater Atlanta Home Builders Association. This program is a well-designed and comprehensive water conservation program developed in partnership by the Atlanta HBA and the Georgia Water Wise Council.

"Dishing Out Dollars,"*Consumer Reports*. March 1998, p.37.
A comprehensive review of energy- and water-efficient dishwashers. www.consumerreports.org

The Resource Guide to Sustainable Landscapes and Gardens, Environmental Resources, Inc., Salt Lake City, Utah. Lists over 1,100 environmentally responsible landscaping materials.

Guide to Resource Efficient Building Elements, 6th Edition, Center for Resourceful Building Technology. Contains a section specifically devoted to landscaping materials; includes supplier lists.

www.toolbase.org
Toolbase Services

Web Resources

www.epa.gov/owm/water-efficiency/toilets.htm
U.S. EPA: Low Flow Toilets
www.conserveh2o.org/smart-tips/LowFlowFixtures.html
Conserve H20: Low Flow Fixtures
www.nsf.org/water.html
NSF International, The Public Health and Safety Company: Water

Interactions

See the following sections for information on how Indoor Water Use affects other building considerations:

OUTDOOR WATER USE

Depending on location, residential water consumption for outdoor use can range between 25 and 200 gallons per day per house, accounting for an average of 50% to 77% of a household's seasonal water use.

Currently, the price paid for water does not necessarily reflect either the costs of purification and treatment or supply and demand. Eastern and midwestern states are depleting their aquifers faster than they are being replenished. A growing number of western states are importers of fresh water. Both trends mean that many communities will continue to spend more money to supply wasteful water habits than they do now. This will require a major expansion of existing infrastructure at an expense of at least several hundred million dollars per state. Home builders can be part of the solution by designing and building homes with lawns, landscaping, irrigation, and drainage plans that use water more efficiently. Using treated water for these purposes puts unnecessary pressure on both natural and municipal resources.

Xeriscaping With Native and Drought-Resistant Plants

Xeriscaping landscape designs concentrate on water conservation by using native plants and avoiding imported species that are not suited to the local climate. They are more likely to survive once the homeowner moves in and require less maintenance, nutrients, fertilizers, and especially, water than many exotic (non-native) species. Plants that are not native but are from areas similar in climate, rainfall, and soil type are preferable to exotic species, providing they are not invasive.

Xeriscaping and Landscaping Planting Plans

Consider xeriscaping and landscape planning early in the design and construction phases of a home. Designing xeriscapes requires 1) knowledge of the plant materials in the site's hardiness zone, 2) knowledge of the interrelationships between plant materials and the environment, 3) an understanding of soil and soil moisture requirements of each plant, 4) understanding of horticulture, and 5) design ability so that the plants fulfill both aesthetic and functional requirements. In many cases, the builder is not involved in the planting portion of the project at all. However, there are several advantages to considering the location and type of plants, grasses, and trees early in the design phase of the project:

- Topsoil can be placed strategically, drainage patterns created, and contours shaped during the backfill and grading phases.
- Adequate holes for planting trees can be dug while a backhoe is on site.

- Provision for landscaping costs can be made early in the project and included in the budget.
- The type and location of the irrigation system can more closely fit the requirements of the vegetation.

A landscape architect can provide useful information about soil type, plant varieties, and light, nutrient, water, and planting requirements. Consult your local nursery, soil or water conservation department, agriculture extension office or university, department of parks, or mail-order nursery and seed companies. All are good sources of information. Information regarding specific plant varieties is also available through local nurseries, soil and water conservation departments, and numerous published sources, as well as through landscape architects.

Minimizing Use of Lawn Turf by Using Native Grasses

Select native grasses (or even buffalo grass or fescue), shrubs, wildflowers, and other groundcovers in lieu of traditional grasses such as Kentucky bluegrass and rye. Native plants can use as little as one fifth the amount of water as their "imported" counterparts. Native species are a water-efficient and attractive way to reduce lawn maintenance and pollution. A traditional well-manicured lawn may require up to 10 pounds of pesticides and fertilizers per acre per year. A two-cycle, gas-powered lawn mower creates as much pollution in 30 minutes as a car driven 172 miles. Replacing resource-intensive turf grasses with native plants, grasses, and wildflowers also aids in the restoration of wildlife and other plants that may be threatened.

The selection of seed or sod is based on a variety of factors: cost, appearance, maintenance requirements, availability, and water requirements. There are no set relationships among these factors; drought-tolerant or lower water-need turf grasses are not necessarily more or less expensive than other grass varieties.

Pervious Materials

Using pervious materials for patios, paths, and driveways allows for natural drainage and enables water to be reabsorbed into the soil, thereby reducing stormwater run-off. Among suitable materials and methods are stone dust, gravel, crushed stone, brick, masonry, grid pavers, pervious concrete pavers, grid-stabilized grass, and combinations of clay and sand as a hard base. Paving stones or brick laid in a pervious material will also allow for more uniform drainage than those set in mortar. Over time, some of these materials will lose their pervious qualities after compaction from use.

Typically, sand, gravel, and crushed stone will be relatively inexpensive. Be sure to border these areas to keep the materials in place. Home buyers should decide whether they prefer loose or hard surfaces for footpaths and driveways.

For homeowners choosing to build their own decks or patios, patios may be a greener option than decks made from CCA (chromated copper arsenate) pressure-treated lumber, which has been phased out by the EPA. Manufacturers cannot use CCA chemicals after December 31, 2003, but this product may still be found in lumber yards. Homeowners should obtain information about more environmentally benign building materials that are suitable for outdoor use. See Chapter 7, Materials, for further information about porch and patio materials.

Irrigation Technology: Timers, Sensors, and Other Controls

Despite perceptions, studies have shown that automated, in-ground sprinkler systems typically use 20% to 30% more water than manual hosing. This is mainly due to overwatering and leaks. Homeowners who insist on a sprinkler system should consider a drip system (see below). Otherwise, they should install programmable switches, timers, or rain sensors to improve the efficiency of the delivery system. Automated irrigation systems that are not responsive to daily watering conditions actually result in an even higher average water use. Separate timers for watering systems run between $30 and $50. Irrigation controllers cost about $40 for the mechanical type and $100 to $150 for digital models.

Drip Irrigation

Drip irrigation systems are the most efficient watering methods available, provided that leaks are minimized. Conventional sprinkler systems lose 30% to 70% of total water to evaporation and runoff. Drip irrigation systems can be on the surface or buried. Surface systems can be installed after home completion by the owner, whereas subsurface systems are completed as part of contractor's landscaping plan. The reduced flow rate and elimination of airborne water delivery makes these systems significantly more efficient. However, their efficiency is dependent on proper installation and elimination of leaks. Another advantage of drip irrigation systems is the lowered potential for leaf mold and mildew growth and weeds because the water is targeted at the root zone of the desirable vegetation. Measures may need to be taken to control root invasion into the drip piping. Drip irrigation systems are not appropriate for lawn areas.

Depending on soil type and the number of emitters, the materials for a drip irrigation system will cost approximately $250 per 1,000 linear feet. Materials are readily available from plumbing suppliers.

Wastewater Treatment and Reclaimed Water

Reclaimed water is one of several forms of water reuse. Specifically, it can be water from a wastewater treatment plant (WWTP) that is diverted into another use, such as landscape irrigation. In some areas of the United States, reclaimed water may be referred to as irrigation quality or "IQ" water. The use of wastewater for nonpotable uses can greatly reduce the demand on potable water sources, and its use is encouraged by many organizations, including FEMP, EPA, and the American Water Works Association.

For a reclaimed water project to be successful, one or more of the following conditions must be present:

- The community lacks an affordable water supply or a high-quality freshwater supply.
- Local public policy encourages or mandates water conservation.
- High-quality effluent is available from a WWTP.
- Reuse is the most cost-effective means of wastewater effluent disposal.

The quality of the reclaimed water must be reviewed to ensure that there will be no adverse effects from long-term use, such as landscape damage due to salt buildup. Note that the use of reclaimed water may be restricted by code.

Rain Catchment

Where codes permit, collected rain water can be used for toilet flushing and landscape and garden irrigation. For watering purposes, a rain catchment or water recovery system can be as simple as roof gutters with downspouts directed into catchment barrels. Rainwater recovery systems attached to some type of distribution system will likely require a pump, and therefore, a filtration system to protect the pump and delivery system. Simple rain barrel systems that connect directly to gutters and have a garden hose outlet range from approximately $100 to $200. All but the simplest rainwater recovery systems are difficult to install as retrofits. Rain catchment systems reduce a homeowner's treated water consumption and reduce stress on local combined sewer systems.

Water Harvesting
In this illustration, rainwater ❶ is collected in a cistern ❷, for controlled release over time ❸.
Illustration: Bruce Hendler

Greywater

Where codes permit, a significant amount of potable water can be readily reused for various nonpotable purposes. Greywater is water from uses such as showers and bathroom sinks that contains a minimum amount of contamination and, with minimal processing, can be used again for non-potable applications such as toilet flushing and non-edible landscape irrigation. Greywater may contain pathogens, and must be treated prior to any reuse. Humans should avoid contact with greywater before treatment. Installation of greywater systems is best done during construction, as retrofits can be difficult.

Case Study: Wastewater Treatment

Although water prices vary greatly around the country, reclaimed water costs significantly less than potable water. For example, in Jupiter, Florida, the price of potable water is now $0.37/1000 liters ($1.70/1000 gallons), versus $0.06/1000 liters ($0.26/1000 gallons) for reclaimed water. Similar pricing differences occur wherever reclaimed water is available.

Efficient Exterior Water Use – Rules of Thumb

- Xeriscaping rather than typical high-water-use landscaping can reduce lawn maintenance, water consumption, and air pollution. Select native trees, plants, and bushes that are drought resistant, suited to your local climate, and capable of contributing to the energy efficiency of a home by shading it from the summer sun and blocking winter winds.
- Select drought-resistant native grasses or other ground covers in lieu of traditional lawn grasses to reduce lawn maintenance and limit water consumption.
- Select pervious surfaces for driveways and pathways.
- Consider installing a rain catchment or greywater system to offset outdoor water use.

Additional Resources

Atienze, J., and J. Craytor, "Plumbing Efficiency through Grey-Water Recycling," *Consulting Specifying Engineer*. March 1995, p. 58.

Farrugia, S., "The Three Rs of Water Conservation," *Consulting Specifying Engineer*. October 1994, p. 18.

Group Raindrops 1995, *Rainwater and You: 100 Ways to Use Rainwater*, Organizing Committee for the Tokyo International Rainwater Utilization Conferences. Sumida City Office Building, 1-23-20 Asumabashi, Sumida City, Tokyo 130, Japan. 1995.

Hightshoe, Gary L.; and Harlen D. Groe, "North American Plant File." Classifies the environmental suitability, aesthetic qualities, cultural requirements, and design uses for 3,600 plants.

Lehr, Valentine A., *"Grey Water Systems,"* Heating/Piping/Air Conditioning. January 1987, p. 103-113.

Rosenbaum, Marc, "Converting 'Waste' into Nutrients—Treating Household Organic Waste." An *Environmental Building News* article on composting toilets. www.buildinggreen.com/features/mr/waste.html

NSF, International Standard 41: *Wastewater Recycled/Reuse and Water Conservation Devices*. www.nsf.org

Rocky Mountain Institute, Water Efficiency; *A Resource Guide for Utility Managers, Community Planners, and Other Decisionmakers*, U.S. EPA Office of Water/Office of Wastewater. 1991.

Water Conservation Plan Guidelines, U.S. Environmental Protection Agency, Office of Water. 1998. EPA-832-D-98-001

Building Greener Building Better, The National Association of Home Builders and the NAHB Research Center, Washington, D.C. 2002.

Web Resources

www.sustainable.doe.gov/index.html
   Sponsored by the U.S. Department of Energy, this site provides information on a number of green building topics, including resource-efficient materials, indoor air quality, waste management, and water efficiency. Case studies of successful projects around the country offer examples of how communities have implemented various strategies.

www.plumbingworld.com
   This company offers plumbing materials and supplies of all kinds for both inside and outside the home. Great for hard-to-find parts and supplies; also offers a line of drip irrigation materials.

www.floridaplants.com
   Although oriented to Florida, this site offers numerous books on all topics from drought-tolerant plants and grasses to landscape design to pest management. In addition to printed publications, there is good information about specific trees, plants, and grasses; soil, water, and light conditions; and disease control. A useful site whether or not you live in Florida.

www.reeusda.gov/1700/statepartners/usa.htm
> The U.S. Department of Agriculture's listing of all the state cooperative/ agriculture extension offices, most of which provide useful information about all types vegetation that is particularly well-suited to climates within your state. Information regarding drip irrigation, organic fertilizers and pest control, and other topics pertinent to reducing water use for the lawn and garden is also available.

www.waterwiser.org
> This site is a good jumping off point for accessing information on all aspects of water conservation. Sites pertaining to water conserving appliances, drip irrigation, xeriscape, landscaping, and community water conservation programs are listed by category.

water.usgs.gov
> The U.S. Geological Survey provides extensive information and data regarding state and regional water use and water quality. In addition to numerous fact sheets, information about the condition of local streams and waterways is also available.

www.terrylove.com/crtoilet.htm
> A Web site that reviews many of the currently available water closets (toilets).

www.concretehomes.com
> The Portland Cement Association provides information on concrete pavers and stained/stamped concrete.

www.gcpa.org
> The Georgia Concrete and Products Association provides information on pervious concrete and other concrete products.

www.toolbase.org
> Toolbase Services

Interactions

See the following sections for information on how Outdoor Water Use affects other building considerations:

Chapter 6 Indoor Environmental Quality

Indoor environmental quality (IEQ) refers to the physical quality of the indoor environment as opposed to its aesthetic quality. A major part of IEQ is indoor air quality (IAQ), but IEQ goes beyond air quality to include acoustics and lighting. The major aspects of IEQ include:

- Indoor air quality (levels of pollutants such as building product emissions, external pollutants, dust, and pollen)
- Humidity (moisture in air)
- Air movement (fresh air and drafts)
- Acoustics (noise transmission between rooms)
- Light intensity and quality (from windows, skylights, and articifial lighting)

Indoor Air Quality

There are four principal ways, in order of priority, to promote acceptable indoor air quality:

1. **Eliminate the source.** This is the method of choice that should be used whenever possible. In a tight home, combustion appliances can "backdraft," meaning gases do not go up the flue or out the vent but are discharged into the home. In exceedingly rare cases a significant amount of flue gas can be discharged into the air. Pressure imbalances, often caused by improper air distribution in the air conditioning system, can create this backdrafting.

   Unvented combustion appliances used for space heating, such as "ventless" fireplaces or unvented kerosene heaters, should never be used in green construction, because they generate unwanted pollutants and can create large amounts of indoor humidity.

   Pressure differences can also induce air to flow into the living space from a garage. Cars, lawn mowers, and appliances in an attached garage can generate exhaust, which gets carried into the home. Garages should be sealed from the remainder of the house with weatherstripping, caulk, and sealants. Special techniques may be needed to prevent radon ("soil gas") from being drawn into the home where site geology presents this problem.

   Use of low-emitting building materials (caulks, sealants, adhesives, particleboard, medium-density fiberboard, and floor coverings, which may emit volatile organic compounds [VOCs] from the plasticizer) can reduce some of the pollutant sources commonly found in new homes, such as paints, stains, finishes, carpeting, and flooring. Green materials are covered in the next chapter. Proper storage of toxic chemicals in sealed containers or outside the living space minimizes this source of irritants.

2. **Ventilate close to the source.** Where polluting or moisture-laden sources must mix with room air, as with gas ranges and bathroom showers, the undesirable air should be exhausted as close as possible to the source. It is beneficial for bath fans and range hoods to operate properly and exhaust to the outdoors. Also, educating occupants to minimize operation of motor vehicles in the garage and ventilating the garage can reduce the build-up of carbon monoxide and other combustion by-products.

3. **Ventilate.** All houses need air exchange to remove stale inside air and excessive moisture. Recently, there has been significant controversy over how much ventilation is needed to maintain indoor air quality. Most experts agree that the solution is not to build a leaky house that relies on infiltration for air exchange, although some air infiltration will always occur. Accidental leaks may create drafts and discomfort. Appropriate levels of air exchange for residents can be provided in a number of ways, for example, spot ventilation, opening a window in a room that is heavily used, heat recovery ventilation, and efficient, whole house ventilation.

4. **Filter.** If the home has an air distribution system, the conventional filter at the fan can be supplemented with specialized filters, discussed in this chapter. If outside air is brought in by a fan as part of a ventilating strategy, it can be filtered as it enters, reducing the intake of pollen and other outdoor irritants. See the "Filtration Techniques" section later in this chapter.

Preventing Pollution From Attached Garages

Attached garages can be sources of indoor air pollutants in homes, especially in rooms that are adjacent to the garage. Combustion by-products from vehicles and lawn equipment pose a danger to home occupants. In homes with attached garages, auto exhaust has been identified as one of the more significant potential sources of indoor pollutants. Stored paints, solvents, and other household chemicals also emit air pollutants. Whenever possible, do not attach the garage directly. Separate the garage from the home entirely, or connect it with a short, covered walkway, garden landscaping area, an enclosed vestibule, or a laundry, mudroom, or workshop.

Attached garages should be sealed from the remainder of the house with weatherstripping, caulk, and sealants. Also, occupants should be educated to minimize operation of motor vehicles in the garage and about the proper storage of paints, solvents, chemicals, and other potential sources of pollutants.

Another alternative is to install a garage exhaust fan. These are usually on a timer or connected to the garage door opener to keep auto exhaust fumes from entering the living areas of the home. The installed cost is generally less than $200.

Radon Control Measures

The U.S. Environmental Protection Agency (EPA) has developed maps that indicate areas with the highest radon potential. The EPA recommends that homes built in areas with high concentrations of radon (areas designated as Zone 1) be built with radon-resistant features. If you elect not to install a radon venting system, consider roughing-in the needed gas-permeable layer of coarse aggregate beneath the slab, and a polyethylene barrier between the aggregate and slab, for future radon venting. Until a house is completed, it is difficult to predict actual radon levels indoors.

Passive radon venting of a slab consists of running a vertical 3" plastic pipe vent from the foundation to the roof through an interior wall. A gas-permeable layer of coarse aggregate should be placed beneath the slab, and a continuous 6-mil polyethylene barrier between the aggregate and slab. The pipe should be stubbed in with a perforated 'T' fitting at the bottom. Pour slab and seal slab joints with caulk. Active venting uses the same system and installation process with an in-line fan installed in the attic to keep a negative pressure in the area beneath the slab. In new homes, passive systems range from $50 to $300. Installing a fan to convert a passive system to an active system typically costs an additional $200. Installing these systems as retrofits in homes without rough-ins can cost three to six times as much.

Radon Resistant Construction

Sample Ventilation Plans

Design 1: Upgraded Spot Ventilation

This relatively simple and inexpensive whole house ventilation system integrates spot ventilation using bathroom and kitchen exhaust fans with an upgraded exhaust fan (usually 100 to 150 cfm) in a centrally located bathroom. When the fan operates, outside air is drawn through inlets in closets with louvered doors. The fan is controlled by a timer set to provide ventilation at regular intervals. Interior doors are undercut to allow air flow to the central exhaust fan. The fan must be a long-life, high-quality unit that operates quietly. In addition to the automatic ventilation provided by this system, occupants can turn on all exhaust fans manually as needed.

Design 2: Whole House Ventilation System

This whole house ventilation system uses a centralized two-speed exhaust fan to draw air from the kitchen, bath, laundry, and living area. The blower is controlled by a timer. The system should provide approximately 0.35 ach on low speed and 1.0 ach on high speed, though lower rates are acceptable for larger homes. Outside air is supplied by a separate dampered duct connected to the return air system. When the exhaust fan operates, the outside air damper opens and allows air to be drawn into the house through the forced-air ductwork.

Design 3: Heat Recovery Ventilation (HRV) System

An air-to-air heat exchanger draws fresh air outside through a duct into the heat exchange equipment and recaptures heating or cooling energy from stale room air as it is being exhausted. Fresh air flows into the house via a separate duct system, which should be sealed as tightly as the HVAC ductwork. Room air can either be ducted to the exchanger from several rooms or a single source. Some HRV units can be wall-mounted in the living area, while others are designed for utility rooms or basements.

Filtration Techniques

Dust, mold spores, pollen, and wood and tobacco smoke can be reduced with an air filtration system. Homes with central forced-air heating and cooling systems have standard furnace filters that protect the air handler's fan motor and keep dust from the heating and cooling coil. They do little to improve air quality. There are four alternative types of residential air filtration systems: electrostatic, electronic, medium-efficiency (including pleated or extended-surface), and high-efficiency particulate air (HEPA).

Pleated filters are inexpensive, can capture mold and pollen, and last twice as long as standard filters. Electrostatic filters can be substituted for standard 1-inch filters; they are efficient at removing larger pollen and mold spores. They are permanently charged filters, which range from $10 to $20 and must be replaced every two to three months. Less expensive reusable/washable electrostatic filters are not recommended. HEPA filters are available for new construction and as retrofits at a cost of up to $500, with replacement filters costing around $50. Electronic air cleaners—also known as electrostatic precipitators and often favored by people with allergies to dust, mold, and pollen—are yet another option, although they are not common in residential applications and need to be cleaned frequently lest they become ineffective.

Combustion Safety

Any device relying solely on natural draft can backdraft, resulting in the release of exhaust gas back into the living space. This occurs when negative pressure is created by a fireplace, exhaust fan, or pressure imbalance (from undersized return air ducts, wind, or stack effect). While backdrafting at significant levels is extremely rare, preventative measures should be considered, including placing the combustion appliance (furnace, boiler, water heater, fireplace, or stove) outside the conditioned space, powering the exhaust with a fan, providing the appliance with its own supply of combustion air, and specifying a sealed combustion appliance with a separate supply and exhaust.

Controlling Indoor Humidity

Ventilation and indoor moisture control strategies are key to safeguarding the quality of indoor air. A home that is neither too dry nor too humid is preferable. When relative humidity drops below 25%, dry skin, nose, throat, and eyes can result. Most tightly built new homes have enough water-generating activities to make dry conditions relatively rare, but humidification may be necessary in dry climates. Relative humidity above 60% while heating or air conditioning can promote damp conditions, and continuous mechanical ventilation in humid climates can load homes with moisture and cause mold growth and structural deterioration.

Build Vented Storage Space for Toxic Materials

Build a storage area outside the living space for chemical and tool storage. Here you can isolate volatile finishing materials, cleaning agents, and petroleum products, thereby eliminating these agents' capacity to degrade the air quality. The added cost of this type of storage area is likely to be modest. Home buyers with children will likely respond positively to the builder's concern for safety. However, it is important home buyers are made aware that if the outside storage area is expected to experience hot or cold temperatures, they must follow all product storage recommendations.

Range Hoods Ducted to the Outside

Kitchen range hood fans vented to the outdoors can control the accumulation of moisture, cooking odors, and combustion by-products (a particularly important consideration for natural gas appliances). General guidelines call for a minimum of 100 cfm for kitchens. Manufacturers should supply a cfm rating for all exhaust fans. Experts generally recommend selecting fans based on an air pressure resistance of 0.25 or 0.30 inches of water rather than 0.1 inches. Kitchen design and cabinet layout affects exhaust fan feasibility and cost. For many sources of moisture, odors, and combustion products (i.e., dishwasher, sink, microwave, portable grill or skillet, toaster, toaster oven, coffee maker, etc.), or where kitchens are open to other rooms, range hoods are not effective and general ventilation must be used.

Don't Oversize

In hot and humid climates, an *essential measure* to control indoor relative humidity is not oversizing the air conditioning equipment. Using the whole building design approach will insure that equipment is designed for the actual cooling load, taking account of energy-saving measures such as low-E glazing. Studies show that it takes nearly five minutes of continuous operation before an air conditioner begins removing moisture from the air. If the system is oversized, it "short-cycles" and seldom runs long enough to remove any humidity. This raises the indoor humidity level, making the home feel damp and clammy, which encourages the occupants to waste energy by keeping the home too cold in an attempt to compensate. It also almost guarantees the growth of mold. Builders should be ready to address buyer anxiety about "undersized" air conditioning with facts and figures. This is one case where bigger is *not* better.

Air Movement

Some homes can be be sited and designed to take advantage of prevailing winds as a cooling and ventilation strategy. Windows, stairwells, and other elements can be located to encourage cross-ventilation throughout the house.

Casement windows have a 90% open area, whereas double hung or sliding windows have less than a 50% open area. Casement windows offer additional advantages because, when properly placed, they help channel breezes into and out of the house. Natural ventilation can help keep houses cool and comfortable at the beginning and end of the cooling season, thereby shortening the times when air conditioning is required.

Adding ceiling fans, which do an excellent job of efficiently moving air, can further reduce the days when air conditioning is needed. Using natural ventilation and ceiling fans together may enable homeowners to set their thermostats up to 4 degrees higher in the cooling season. A ceiling fan should have a minimum clearance of 10 inches

Ceiling Fan Sizes	
Largest Room Dimension	Minimium Fan Dimension (inches)
12 feet or less	36
12–16 feet	48
16–17.5 feet	52
17.5–18.5 feet	56
18.5 or more feet	2 fans

between the ceiling and the fan to provide adequate ventilation in a standard room with 8-foot ceilings. In rooms with higher ceilings, fans should be mounted about 8 feet above the floor.

Air Sealing

Air sealing is discussed fully in Chapter 3, The Building Envelope, "Insulation and Air Sealing." Air sealing also affects indoor environmental quality in several ways:

Controlling humidity. Air sealing reduces leakage, which avoids excessively dry indoor conditions in winter. It also allows the home to stay dehumidified in hot, humid weather, avoiding mold growth and clammy indoor conditions.

Preventing mold growth. Air sealing helps minimize the random flow of air through the building envelope. This in turn minimizes the chances that humid air (from inside in winter or outside in hot-humid conditions) will contact and wet a cold surface, with the potential of causing mold growth if the condition persists for long periods.

Reducing drafts. Indoor environmental quality is improved substantially if drafts are eliminated in winter conditions. This is reflected in the design of air distribution systems, which can be simpler and more effective if they don't have to compensate for drafts.

Acoustics

One frequently overlooked aspect of indoor environmental quality is acoustics. The smaller the home, the more important is acoustic isolation between rooms. Improving the acoustics in your model home could be used to advantage as a sales tool. Among the major issues involved are:

Avoiding air leakage. Relatively small air leaks can transmit sound very efficiently through partitions. It is important first to block air leaks between adjacent rooms before investing in measures that reduce sound conduction. The most common leaks are through doorways, around electrical outlets and under the wall sill plate.

Conduction through walls. In general, the conduction of higher-frequency sound (high-pitched voices, music, etc.) can be suppressed by isolating the wall surfaces from each other. One common method is to hang the gypsum board on one side of the wall on acoustical channels. Another method is to use separate studs for each side of the wall. It helps to insert cellulose or fiber glass within the wall. Any insulation in the wall cavity will help reduce sound transmission.

Transmission through floors. In addition to closing off leaks and suppressing high-frequency air-borne sound with isolation, impact noise needs to be controlled in floor systems. This can be done by inserting an impact-absorbing layer under the flooring.

Sound rooms. Increasingly popular in higher-end homes are sound rooms, set up for stereo and video presentations, sometimes with theater-type seating. These rooms should be carefully engineered to keep sounds from being transmitted throughout the home.

Sound through ductwork. When acoustical isolation is important, ducts should be relatively long, and should be lined with acoustical duct liner. Locate air handling units carefully to avoid noise pollution in areas of concern, such as bedrooms. Design the ductwork and locate the interior air handler or furnace to minimize noise transmission to living spaces.

Equipment-generated sound. One common source of annoying sound is the outdoor section of the air conditioning unit. This device has a fan and a compressor, both of which can create noise.

Appliance-generated sound. While most modern dishwashers and refrigerators are remarkably quiet, energy-efficient, higher-cost units tend to be *very* quiet, an added plus to their efficiency and style.

Planning for acoustics. Home buyers typically are influenced by their initial impression, and so can be "wowed" by large, continuous open spaces. Open plans have their place, but having at least two living spaces that can be acoustically separated is a useful strategy when raising children, especially teenagers, or when there are two unrelated people sharing a house. This amenity needs to be pointed out to potential buyers.

Bath fans. Larger fans generally cost more but also last longer, run quieter, and allow for placement farther away from the living area, which in turn lessens noise problems. Larger, quieter fans typically cost $80 to $90 more than standard units.

Light Intensity and Quality

Energy-efficient lighting and daylighting tips are discussed in Chapter 4, Energy Efficiency, "Lighting." The intensity and quality of lighting are design issues that have an impact on environmental quality. Typically, a low level of background lighting, possibly indirect, should be coupled with focused "task lighting" that illuminates reading and work areas. It is both energy-wasting and unpleasant to over-light a large area, although many people rely on bright lighting to be able to see. Lighting controls are important, to allow selected lights to be dimmed or turned off. For example, it is desirable to be able to turn down the lights over the food preparation area while eating, if (as is very common in today's plans) the cooking and eating areas are in the same space.

Fireplaces and Stoves

Wood-burning fireplaces and stoves may be replaced by less polluting and more efficient gas or electric units. A typical gas fireplace is a sealed combustion unit. If a wood stove does not draw in its own combustion air, a supply of outside air near the stove is essential to prevent the stove's exhaust from backdrafting other appliances. A wood-burning fireplace is required by code to always have a separate supply of outside air delivered into the firebox, preferably inside a set of glass doors that can be closed to improve efficiency.

Sealed Combustion Furnaces or Boilers

Most furnaces are nondirect-vent units, meaning they use surrounding air for combustion. Other units are direct-vent (including power-vented and sealed-combustion) furnaces and include condensing models. They bring combustion air into the burner area via inlets that extend to the home's exterior. Condensing, sealed-combustion furnaces carry an installed-cost premium of around $500. Natural draft equipment is safe and approved by code. Nondirect-vent furnaces do have the potential to backdraft or otherwise leak carbon monoxide into the living space. If it occurs, which is rare, it can result in potentially serious health problems. Furnace mechanical rooms can also be sealed from other rooms in the house. Insulate both the interior and exterior walls. Install two outside-air ducts (sized specifically for the furnace) from outside into the furnace room, with one opening near the floor and the other near the ceiling, or as otherwise specified by local codes.

Sealed Mechanical Room Design

Screened high and low ventilation ducts into mechanical room

Ventilated attic

Insulated and sealed walls between mechanical room and home

Mechanical room access door is solid (non-louvered) with weatherstripping and a tight threshold.

Sealed Combustion Water Heaters

Fuel-fired water heaters should be located in conditioned spaces that are isolated (in terms of pressure and air leakage) from the living area. Examples include crawlspaces, attics, and unconditioned basements. If fuel-fired water heaters are located in interior spaces, such as interior mechanical rooms connected to conditioned spaces or laundry rooms, consider providing air sealing and R-11 insulation. Also consider including provisions for outside combustion air, such as those deployed for a direct-vent unit. Direct-vent units have a double flue pipe that includes both an intake for combustion air and a flue for exhaust gas. Because they use forced-air blowers, some units can be vented out the sidewall of the home, rather than through the roof. Note that some sealed combination units do not operate as well in high wind areas. Sealed combustion water heaters carry a cost premium of approximately $300 to $500. A more common and less expensive alternative to sealed combustion is "power-venting," where a fan creates a stronger draft that is secure against backdrafting.

Bathroom Exhaust Strategies

Bath exhaust fans can be set to a timer or hard wired for 24-hour operation as part of a whole house ventilation strategy. Whenever possible, select a fan that has been tested to deliver its rated output under normal conditions. Also, the high-efficiency motors used in quiet "low-sone" fans will use less electricity when operated continuously and are nearly silent. All bath fans should be vented to the outdoors and not discharged into an attic or crawlspace, where the moisture exhausted can cause serious damage to the home's structure.

Indoor Environmental Quality – Rules of Thumb

- Alternatives to traditional attached garages, such as detached garages or locked, vented storage spaces, help prevent exhaust gas and chemical gases and vapors from entering the home.
- Pursue moisture control techniques to minimize mold growth.
- Open-hearth fireplaces are not recommended. Installed fireplaces should have their own appropriately sized, direct-air supply, as well as tight-fitting glass doors.
- Fuel-fired appliances, furnaces, and water heaters should be located in insulated spaces that are outside the air envelope of the living area.
- Consider upgrading the air infiltration systems by using pleated, electrostatic, electronic, or HEPA filtration.
- To reduce offgassing, use tacks rather than adhesives when securing carpet.
- Rough-in or install radon venting systems.

Additional Resources

"Air Sealing," *Technology Fact Sheet*, Office of Building Technology, State and Community Programs, Energy Efficiency and Renewable Energy, U.S. Department of Energy. February 2000. 800-DOE-3732; www.eere.energy.gov/

Builder's Guide to Energy Efficient Homes in Georgia, Southface Energy Institute, Inc., Atlanta, Georgia. September 1999.

A Guide to Developing Green Builder Programs, NAHB Research Center. February 2000.

Web Resources

www.energybuilder.com
>The Building Environmental Science and Technology Web site provides information on a wide range of green building topics, as well as a good overview of IEQ concerns and ways to mitigate potential problems in the home.

www.epa.gov/iaq/homes/index.html
>The U.S. Environmental Protection Agency Web site contains information on many indoor air quality topics: specific contaminants and pollutants, exposure, risk, and mitigation.

www.epa.gov/iaq/radon/zonemap.html
>Provides the EPA's radon zone map referenced earlier in this chapter.

www.lungusa.org/air/air_indoor_redux2.html
>The American Lung Assocation's indoor air quality checklist.

www.toolbase.org/docs/ToolBaseTop/Research/4021_techscan3-10.pdf
>Toolbase: Indoor Environmental Quality

www.greenguard.org
>The GREENGUARD® Environmental Institute

Interactions

See the following chapters for information on how Indoor Environmental Quality affects other building considerations:

Chapter 7 Materials

Selecting Green Materials

Optimizing material selection is a key component of building a green home that minimizes its use of resources while providing improved energy performance and better indoor environmental quality. Environmentally friendly building materials are a growing and dynamic field, with more choices available every year. This chapter will address key issues and approaches to material selection and will refer builders to more detailed discussions, tools, and listings of materials.

Material selection is a complex process involving many variables, and there is rarely one best method that can be used across the board to select materials. Green material selection typically involves an assessment of a product's life cycle environmental impacts. This process tracks the raw materials used to produce a material, its production process, its transportation, its characteristics in use, and its disposal, reuse, or recycling options. Through the life cycle assessment process, a number of green attributes have been identified for various construction materials. The following attributes are included as an introduction to key green factors that builders should consider when assessing different construction products (see "What is Green?" later in this chapter).

Renewability refers to materials that are rapidly renewable and are derived from biological resources such as trees and agricultural products. Examples include natural linoleum, cork, bamboo, straw-based board products (equivalent to cabinet-grade particleboard or medium-density fiberboard), and some types of wood and engineered wood products. These products can be cost competitive and comparable in performance to nonrenewable building products. Some may be biodegradable at the end of their useful life.

Recycled content includes both *post-consumer* and *pre-consumer* (also known as *post-industrial*) content. Materials with recycled content are available for many types of building products, often with competitive, comparable, or better performance than materials made from virgin materials. Post-consumer content, which refers to materials that have been recovered from home or office waste streams, provides greater environmental benefits than pre-consumer/post-industrial.

Reusability/recyclability describes how easily a product may be reused or recycled once it has reached the end of its service life. Products that can be more easily disassembled or separated from adjacent materials for reuse or recycling should be considered. Look for products that are collected by recycling centers, such as cardboard, glass, plastics, or metal, or that come from manufacturers sponsoring take-back programs for their materials.

Durability of a material describes what the expected maintenance and service life of a product may be. Low-maintenance products with long service lives are typically preferred by home buyers and merit particular attention.

Embodied energy is the energy required to extract, process, package, transport, install, and recycle or dispose of materials that make up the building. Up to 70% of the total energy invested in a building's construction is embodied in the materials themselves. Because the energy consumed to transport materials is often a significant portion of its embodied energy, locally produced materials are preferable to materials that must be shipped long distances.

Embodied Energy of Building Materials

Environmental impact can be considered in two ways. In one respect, it refers to the effect a material has on the indoor environmental quality within a home. In a broader context, it refers to a material's effect on the outdoor environment and atmosphere. To create a healthy indoor environment, select materials that limit offgassing, have minimal or no toxic properties, and do not shed dust or fiber. For the outdoor environment, select materials that minimize impacts on ozone depletion and global warming (e.g., products that do not contain HCFCs, halons, etc.) and minimize the release of toxic waste.

Material Reuse

Consider reusing lumber scraps such as 2x wood cutoffs for bridging, stakes, bracing, shims, drywall nailers, and blocking. Similarly, cutoff sheathing waste can be used for drywall stops and furring.

Consider setting up an in-place concrete recycling system (to create aggregate) in larger projects.

Misordered, excess, or slightly damaged finished building products can be reused at the jobsite, donated for a tax deduction to nonprofit building supply centers, or transported to another jobsite. The same may be true for commodity items such as drywall and framing, if they are not damaged and if an outlet for used building materials is available.

Reuse packaging materials whenever possible. For example, reuse cardboard for your packing and transportation needs. Some product manufacturers also take back pallets or other packing materials for reuse or recycling.

How to Find Green Material Suppliers

Green building product information can be found in periodicals, books and other resource guides, and Web sites. A number of organizations monitor the market for new products, evaluate the performance of new and evolving products, and— perhaps most important—identify green product suppliers. Two leading resources are the *Environmental Building News'* *GreenSpec* and the National Center for Appropriate Technology's (NCAT) *Guide to Resource Efficient Building Elements.*

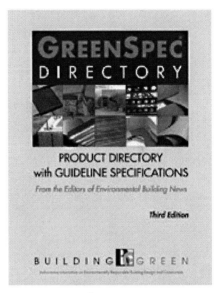

For more information, contact *Environmental Building News* **(802-257-7300; www.buildinggreen.com) and NCAT's Center for Resourceful Building Technology (406-549-7678; www.crbt.org).**

In the GreenSpec Directory, the editors of *Environmental Building News* have carefully screened information on more than 1,750 green building products. Here you will find product descriptions, environmental characteristics and considerations, and manufacturer contact information organized according to the 16-division CSI MasterFormat™ system. The directory listings cover more than 250 categories of building products. The GreenSpec Directory does not rely on any industry or manufacturer fees for production. Information included in the document is dependable and unbiased.

Both the GreenSpec Directory and NCAT Guide have extensive materials information and supplier listings and have served as sources for some of the descriptions provided below.

Green Materials by Category

Green products and systems are continually coming onto the market. The pages that follow contain a limited listing of green products that have been used for a number of years.

Foundations

Concrete containing recycled waste (slag cement, flyash, aggregate).
Concrete with flyash and other recycled waste can be cost competitive with
regular concrete and is available in many locations. Concrete with flyash
sets up somewhat more slowly, but is easy to work with and has a slightly
smoother finish. Flyash can typically replace 15% to 25% of the Portland
cement in a conventional concrete mix (in some cases, the replacement rate
can be 35% or higher). Slag cement can typically replace 30% to 70% of the
Portland cement in a concrete mix. Aggregates (typically sand and gravel)
are mixed with water and cement to make concrete. Recycled concrete or
other recycled materials can be used as aggregate or fill material.

Autoclaved cellular concrete (ACC). ACC is a lightweight, precast concrete
product typically manufactured as blocks or panels. The ACC process uses
steam-cured hydrogen bubbles to create an insulating material that can be
worked with regular tools. Atypical solid 8-inch ACC block wall may
achieve R-19.

Insulating Concrete Forms (ICFs). Lightweight, interlocking, rigid foam
blocks or panels can be used as a permanent concrete form for foundations.
These hollow assemblies are filled with reinforced
concrete similar to traditional concrete foundations.
However, the foam forms remain in place, acting as
high-performance insulation and as an attachment
point for finishes. Because of the modular nature of
the blocks and the known volume of concrete inside
them, little waste of either material is generated.
Concrete is a locally derived material and can incorporate recycled or post-industrial by-products such
as flyash or slag cement. Recently, other insulating
concrete wall systems have come onto the market,
including precast and insulated cast-in-place as-
sembles.

**Insulated concrete
forms
(Photo courtesy of
www.ci.austin.tx.us/
greenbuilder)**

Non-asphalt based damp proofing. Synthetic rubber and cement-based damp
proofing products are available that do not contaminate soil and ground
water. Polyethylene-based damp proofing products typically contain a significant percentage of post-consumer recycled materials.

Frost-Protected Shallow Foundation (FPSF). A frost-protected shallow foundation (FPSF) is a green technology that conserves resources, reduces distur-
bance of the soil, speeds construction, and reduces construction costs by several thousand dollars on a typical house. In the past, most buildings in cold
climates have been protected from frost damage by starting the foundation
below the frost line or founding it on solid rock. In contrast, FPSFs use polystyrene insulation board to retain heat under foundations, and in that way,
to raise the frost line. FPSFs as little as 12 inches below grade are protected
from damaging frost heave, even where the design frost depth is 15 feet or
more.

FPSFs for heated build-
ings keep ground tem-
peratures above freez-
ing by retaining heat
from the building.
FPSFs for unheated
buildings and struc-
tures have insulation
under the entire slab
and foundation wall

FPSF

Conventional

and extending several feet beyond. Thicker
insulation is used to retain heat that is in the deep
ground below the structure and can be used on
attached garages, porches, and freestanding buildings, posts, and walls.

FPSF designs are available for slab-on-grade foundations, crawlspaces, and
walk-out basements. They are widely used for homes, low-rise apartments,
and commercial buildings as well as remodeling additions.

More than 1.5 million FPSFs have been built in the United States, Canada,
and Scandinavia over the past 50 years. U.S. research and development
has been conducted by the NAHB Research Center under grants from the
Society of the Plastics Industry, the U.S. Department of Housing and Urban
Development, and the U.S. Department of Energy's National Renewable
Energy Laboratory. Necessary climate data has been prepared by the
National Climatic Data Center of the National Oceanic and Atmospheric
Administration (NOAA) working with the NAHB Research Center.

Walls and Floors

Engineered lumber. Manufactured laminated veneer lumber, laminated
strand lumber, glue-laminated lumber, and truss-joist I-beams offer consis-
tent performance, predictable quality, and superior structural characteristics.
Engineered lumber consists of small pieces of wood combined with adhesives
under heat and pressure to produce practical and economical alternatives to
solid wood framing in headers, beams, and joists. Engineered lumber techniques include the following:

- **Substitute engineered lumber for 2 x 10s or larger.** Avoid using 2 x 10s
  and 2 x 12s as they often come from old growth forests.
- **Use engineered lumber for headers and beams.** Manufactured laminated veneer lumber and laminated strand lumber are stronger than
  dimensional lumber of the same size and are well-suited to replace solid
  or built-up headers.
- **Use wood I-joists for floors and ceilings.** I-joists have a high strength-
  to-weight ratio and provide structural support for floors and roofs, while
  only using one third of the material required for traditional solid joist
  systems.

Steel framing is increasingly popular in residential construction.

Light gauge steel framing. Steel framing (studs and floor systems) has many advantages: it contains a minimum of 25% recycled material and is 100% recyclable. There is typically less scrap and waste; a steel frame house accounts for little more than 1 cubic foot of steel scrap. Steel is noncombustible and is not vulnerable to termites and mold and therefore may contribute to improved indoor air quality. Steel framing can be substituted "stick for stick," or specific "steel techniques" can be employed to use less steel. Substituting steel for wood is appropriate in non-load-bearing interior partitions. Standard details and load tables are available online at www.steelframingalliance.com. Pay attention to ensure a thermal break is provided to avoid thermal bridging.

A finished house with steel framing does not appear different from any other home. One great advantage is that the framing will not deflect, bend, or warp over time.

Structural insulated panels (SIPs) for walls and roofs. SIPs are most often OSB sheathing laminated to expanded polystyrene foam cores and are designed to take the place of traditional stick framing. The product is produced in large panels, which can be ordered from the manufacturer in standard or custom sizes with window and door openings already cut in place. SIPs create energy-efficient, quiet homes due to tight construction and the uniformity of the insulation layer. Initial savings in framing and the labor typically required to insulate and gap seal may be offset by learning curve costs or slightly higher material costs.

Insulating Concrete Forms (ICFs). ICFs are foam insulation formwork for reinforced concrete walls. These permanent forms stay in place after the initial pouring of the concrete core, providing insulation, finish attachment surfaces, and a chase for utilities. ICFs typically accept all traditional finishes, including siding, stucco, brick, plaster, and drywall. Benefits to the homeowner include high thermal and acoustical performance, low air filtration, disaster and termite resistance, and extremely long durability. Construction costs for ICF homes average about 2% to 5% more than traditionally framed homes. Lightweight, interlocking blocks or panels are easily cut-to-fit with common hand-tools and set in place with little to no waste. ICF construction training is readily available through regional manufacturers.

Forestry and Lumber Programs

The Sustainable Forestry Initiative® (SFI) program. The Sustainable Forestry Initiative® program is a comprehensive system of principles, objectives, and performance measures developed by professional foresters, conservationists, and scientists (among others) that combines the perpetual growing and harvesting of trees with the long-term protection of wildlife, plants, soil, and water quality. There are currently over 136 million acres of forestland in

North America enrolled in the SFI® program, making it among the world's largest sustainable forestry programs.

FSC-certified lumber. The Forest Stewardship Council (FSC) certification system ensures that an independent evaluation has been performed on a forest company's practices based on rigorous, publicly available forest management standards. These include long-term economic viability, protection of biodiversity, conservation of ancient natural woodland, long-term responsible management, recognition of indigenous peoples' and forest workers' rights, and regular monitoring. The FSC is the only system that verifies claims from the forest to the final product, a process known as "chain of custody" monitoring. Select lumber and other forest products that carry the FSC registered trademark whenever possible in order to support responsible forestry and provide forest owners with an incentive to maintain and improve forest management practices.

Wall Cladding / Exterior Finishes

Recycled-content siding. Alternatives to wood siding include siding with recycled content, such as aluminum and wood fiber. Aluminum siding has high recycled content and is itself recyclable but has high embodied energy. Engineered and composite wood siding is a combination of post-industrial wood fiber and resin. Coating and pre-finishing the siding enhances weather resistance and durability. When choosing siding, seek recycled products that use post-industrial scrap in the manufacturing process.

Fiber-cement siding and exterior trim. Fiber-cement siding and trim is durable, impact resistant, moisture resistant, and termite resistant. It also inhibits fungus growth, is noncombustible, and is easy to install and finish. However, most fiber-cement products use long wood fibers imported from overseas. Installers must be careful when sawing the material. Masks are recommended to avoid inhaling harmful dust and particles.

Engineered wood trim. Exterior wood trim material is available in finger-jointed and glued stock fabricated from several species of wood, such as pine and redwood. These materials are made from smaller pieces of wood, allowing the use of smaller, sustainably harvested trees. These products are typically available preprimed, thus ensuring durability and saving labor.

Recycled plastic lumber. Recycled plastic lumber is produced in a wide variety of sizes and colors for use in decks, fences, landscaping, countertops, and exterior furniture. Most are made from 90% to 100% post-consumer plastics such as HDPE and LDPE, while composite products are made from post-consumer plastics and wastewood fibers. Avoid using virgin plastic lumber. All recycled plastic lumber should have a label prominently displayed.

Traditional Portland Cement Stucco. Traditional Portland Cement Stucco (not to be confused with EIFS, which, unlike stucco, does allow moisture to escape) can be applied to masonry, concrete, or framed walls. Stucco is made from materials that are extracted and manufactured regionally.

Patios vs. decks. Patios may be more environmentally friendly than decks, because they require fewer materials and resources to construct. When built out of bricks, concrete, or traditional masonry, patios are more durable and weather resistant and typically require less maintenance. For decks, consider the following options: recycled plastic lumber and recycled wood–polymer composite lumber (both products look good and are far more durable and low-maintenance than wood); reclaimed, decay-resistant woods such as reclaimed redwood; or sustainably harvested, decay-resistant woods.

Roofs

Light-colored roofing. Some light colored roofing materials can increase solar reflectance values, meaning more of the sun's energy is reflected and less absorbed into the home. This can reduce cooling requirements by as much as 20%. Higher solar reflectance can be achieved with light-colored roofing materials such as tiles, painted metal, shingles, and white-reflective membranes and coatings.

Recycled-content organic asphalt shingles. Recycled-content organic asphalt shingles have characteristics similar to those of fiber glass asphalt shingles: they are lightweight and come with warranties of up to 30 years. However, they also contain recycled waste paper and/or use reclaimed mineral slag in their aggregate surface.

Long-lasting roofing: tile and slate. Tile and slate roofing materials are very durable, are easy to maintain, and have good fire ratings. Larger structural systems may be required to support the higher weight of tile and slate.

Metal roofing. Metal roofing made from steel, aluminum, or copper is durable and low maintenance. The components come in many sizes and shapes, including panels, shingles, shakes, and tiles. Some products contain up to 100% recycled material, and many products can be recycled. Avoid metal roofing where lead is used in the alloy or coating.

Insulation and Air Sealing

When sealing duct work joints, mastic is the best choice. If using tape, make sure it meets UL-181.

Air sealing materials. Look for low-VOC compounds, specifically, caulk, sealant, glue, tape, mastic, spray foam, and other related products. For large penetrations, consider reduced toxicity spray foams rather than batt insulation. Use noncombustible sealants between floors and between the living space and attic. Installers should check with the manufacturers for safe work practices when installing insulation.

Insulation Types

Batt Insulation
- Least expensive option
- Look for 30% recycled content.
- Always include sealing to reduce air flow.
- Check VOC offgassing rating to get lowest levels.

Blown-in Insulation
- Spray or dry pack
- More than 80% recycled content
- Helps reduce infiltration.
- Insist on borate-treated cellulose only, not ammonium sulfate.
- Fiber glass or cellulose or rock wool

Rigid Foam
- Typically closed cell installed on the exterior as sheathing
- Good for reducing heat loss/gain through studs
- Can serve as moisture drainage plane (with proper installation!)
- Used in wall, roof, and basement applications

Spray Foam
- Very high R-values possible
- Excellent for sealing the envelope tightly
- Great for irregular spaces
- Most expensive option
- Available in low or high density

Recycled Cotton Batts
- Made from recycled blue jean material
- Doesn't "itch"
- No IAQ problems
- Limited availability
- Potentially expensive

Windows

The National Fenestration Rating Council (NFRC) Web site (www.nfrc.org) is a valuable resource for builders. The NFRC-certified rating or label describes certain physical properties of the entire window, not just the glass: the U factor, the Solar Heat Gain Factor (SHGF), and the Visible Transmittance (VT). Air leakage data may also be provided from another source (see Chapter 2, Renewable Energy, Passive Solar Design Strategies for more extensive discussion).

The wide array of more environmentally friendly window frames and glazing products is described below.

Window frames. Some builders prefer the look and feel of wood window frames, while others prefer the lower maintenance of aluminum or vinyl frames. Clad frames with wood interiors and a thin, more weather-resistant cladding on the exterior are an excellent green choice because they combine the advantages of wood and vinyl or metals. For energy efficiency reasons, non-thermally broken metal frames are not typically recommended, unless you are building in a climate with mild winters. In other climates, metal frames must have a thermal break sash, and frames made of "pultruded fiber glass" are gaining in popularity.

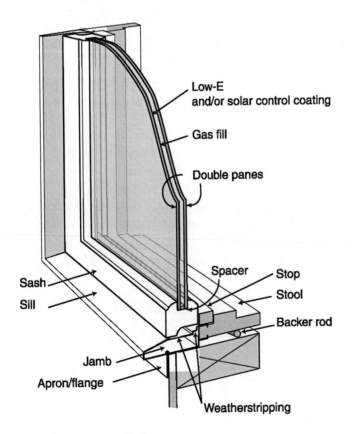

Low-E and/or solar control coating

Gas fill

Double panes

Spacer Stop

Stool

Sash

Sill

Backer rod

Jamb

Apron/flange

Weatherstripping

Energy-efficient window technologies are available to produce windows with the U-factor, SHGC, and VT properties needed for any application.

High-performance window glazing. For most climates, double-pane windows are essential to reduce heat loss or heat gain. Other glazing options that increase thermal performance include low-emissivity (low-e) films that reflect heat into or away from the building, depending on climate; argon or krypton gas, which is used between panes to lower conductivity and increase R-value; and "Heat Mirror," a clear low-e film used between window panes to create a greater number of insulative chambers within the window.

Light pipes: Light pipes transmit natural daylight into interior and otherwise dark spaces through highly reflective, insulated cylinders. Daylight is channeled to a light diffuser in the ceiling, which provides natural daylight, increases comfort, and enhances indoor environments.

ENERGY STAR®–rated windows are tailored to fit the energy needs of the country's three main climate regions: Northern, Central, and Southern.

Finishes

Low- or no-VOC (volatile organic compound) interior latex paint. Many latex paints are available with low amounts of organic solvent. Select latex paints that also have low or no VOCs. These paints have lower odors and emissions when wet or newly dried. Latex paint is generally nonflammable, has lower toxicity than oil-based paints, and can be cleaned up with water.

Low-VOC, water-based wood finishes. Water-based, formaldehyde-free, nonflammable, low-odor, and low-VOC content wood finishes are available in gloss, semi-gloss, satin, and solid finishes for interior applications. These products are easy to clean up as well as fast drying, which reduces down-time between coats.

Natural paint. Natural paints, made from milk protein, plant, or mineral-based compounds, can be a viable alternative to conventional paints. Natural paints are not necessarily low-VOC, as some types are organic and solvent-based, and contain isoaliphatic hydrocarbons. Some paints use citrus oil solvents, which dry quickly; however, they may cause allergies or irritation in environmentally sensitive individuals.

Recycled-content and/or formaldehyde-free interior panels. Choose from a variety of recycled-content and/or formaldehyde-free panel materials for millwork, cabinets, and paneling. These include formaldehyde-free medium density fiberboard (MDF), panels made from post-consumer and post-industrial corrugated boxes and newspapers, and panels made from agricultural waste such as wheat, straw, and soy. Some panels are available in sizes up to 5' x 18' with thicknesses of ¼" to 1¼".

Finger-jointed trim. Finger-jointed trim is made from short lengths of lumber formerly scrapped or burned for fuel. Finger-jointed trim will need to be painted, and some products have a hardwood veneer well suited for stain or other finishes.

Environmental considerations for selecting flooring. Environmentally preferable flooring materials have one or more of the following characteristics: they produce low emissions, are made from rapidly renewable and/or natural resources, contain recycled content, are recyclable, require little maintenance, and/or do not require toxic cleaners to maintain.

General carpet information. Carpet systems, including carpets, carpet cushions, and carpet adhesives, can emit significant levels of VOCs, particularly during and immediately after installation. The Carpet and Rug Institute of Dalton, Georgia, has established a Green Label testing program that sets emission thresholds for VOCs, formaldehyde, and other compounds found in carpets, cushions, and adhesives. Carpet selections should meet or exceed these standards. Carpet must also be properly maintained to control dust, antigens from dust mites, and potential microbial growth (often the result of excessive moisture from leaks, spills, etc.). Carpet cleaners should also use low-emission formulations where available.

Recycled-content carpet. Post-consumer products (such as soda bottles) containing polyethylene terephthalate (PET) are recycled into polyester carpet face fiber, thereby minimizing landfill waste, air pollution, and the fuel required for producing virgin fiber. PET is inherently stain-resistant and is more hydrophobic than nylon. Where additional durability is required, a growing number of nylon carpets are available that incorporate recycled content into their face fibers or backings.

For padding, consider synthetic felted pad made from carpet manufacturing waste, natural fiber wool or jute, foamed pads made from true natural rubber, or foamed pads manufactured without the use of ozone-depleting chemicals.

Flooring from rapidly renewable materials. Bamboo and cork flooring are long lasting, sustainable flooring alternatives. Controlled bamboo forests mature in three to five years and typically produce as much flooring as a hardwood forest does after 40 years. Installing bamboo is similar to installing hardwood floors. Cork flooring is harvested from the bark of the cork tree, which grows back completely in 9 to 14 years. Cork has natural fire resistance, is resilient, will not rot, is hypoallergenic, and provides insulation and cushioning. Cork wear layers can be waxed, varnished, and coated with polyurethane or acrylic.

Recycled-content ceramic tile. Recycled content ceramic tiles are available in a wide variety of styles, colors, and finishes. Installation and cost are often similar to non-recycled tiles. Some contain as much as 85% post-consumer recycled glass.

Natural linoleum. Natural linoleum is made primarily of natural raw materials: linseed oil, rosins, and wood flour combined with a natural jute backing. Linoleum is highly resistant and over time becomes harder and more durable, while remaining quiet and comfortable underfoot.

Case Study: Material Savings / Framing Techniques

Software: SoftPlan Systems, Brentwood, TN
Builder: Caruso Homes, Crofton, MD
House type: 2,300 square feet, single family detached

Estimating software was used to quantify the material savings of selected efficient framing techniques.

Technique	Savings[1]
Accurate take-off tools	$595
Increased spacing of floor joists from 12" to 19.2"	$412[2]
Modular roof design	$194
House configuration (modular overall dimensions)	$124
Reduced header sizes	$39

1   Savings based on lumber prices from mid-Atlantic region, March 1996.
2   Because the builder typically uses 3/4" floor sheathing, the increased joint spacing did not require thicker floor sheathing.

Source: NAHB Research Center's *Residential Construction Waste Management – A Builder's Field Guide.*

Case Study: Material Savings / Value-Engineering Techniques

Software: Argos Systems, Bedford, MA
Builder: DeLuca Enterprises, Newtown, PA
House type: 2,300 square feet, single family detached

Estimating software was used to quantify the material savings of selected value-engineering techniques.

Technique	Savings[1]
In-line framing spaced at 24" o.c.	$960
Increased spacing of floor joists from 16" to 24"	$747[2]
Reduced header sizes	$162
Relocating four windows and doors	$45
Ladder framing at intersecting walls	$45
Two-stud and backer corner framing	$30

1   Savings based on lumber prices from mid-Atlantic region, March 1996.
2   Because the builder typically uses 3/4" floor sheathing, the increased joint spacing did not require thicker floor sheathing.

Source: NAHB Research Center's *Residential Construction Waste Management – A Builder's Field Guide.*

The following article appeared in the October 2003 issue of *The Journal of Light Construction*. To order a subscription, call 800/375-5981 or visit our website at www.jlconline.com.

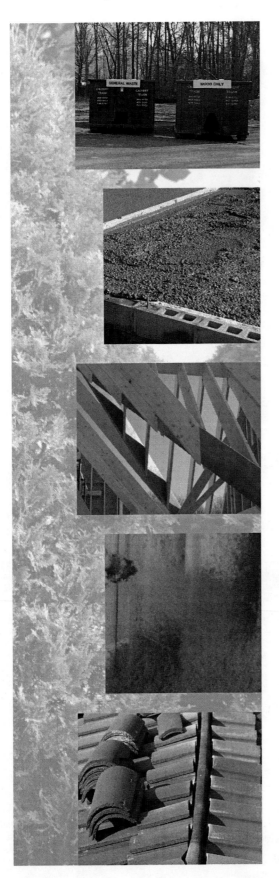

What is Green?

by Alex Wilson

Determing a building product's true environmental impact is not always easy

Readers of *The Journal of Light Construction* are no strangers to the green building movement. There are now several dozen residential green building programs around the country with thousands of homes built in the past few years to their standards. Many of you participate in those programs, or have launched your own green marketing efforts.

Energy Star Homes, which focuses on energy efficiency, has seen a dramatic surge in participation, with over 100,000 homes built through the program. Even the National Association of Home Builders—far from a fringe environmental advocacy group—has taken an active interest in green building, with the formation of a green building subcommittee and the passage of a green building policy last May.

A key aspect of green home building is the selection of green building products—materials that carry a minimal environmental impact. But just what makes a given product "green"? How do you evaluate the relative greenness of different products? How do you find green products? How do you distinguish the truly green from the greenwash?

We at BuildingGreen, Inc., and *Environmental Building News* have been researching and writing about green building products for more than ten years. We've come up with specific criteria for evaluating building products and identifying those we consider green—a process we use in screening products for our GreenSpec directory. Here's what we've come up with.

What is Green? (continued)

Defining Green

Evaluating building products for their "greenness" involves something called "life-cycle assessment" (LCA). This is an emerging science that considers a product's environmental burdens throughout its life cycle—from resource extraction, through manufacturing and use, and ultimately to disposal or recycling into a new product. Because most building materials are in use for a long time, the use phase of a material's LCA is particularly important.

To complicate matters in LCA work, we consider lots of different types of impacts. We consider impacts on the resource base—harvesting timber, for example, or extracting mineral ores. We consider air pollution and water pollution emissions during manufacture and shipping, one measure of which is the "embodied energy" of a material. We consider what effect a product may have on the operation of a building—for example, the product's impact on the energy use of the building or the maintenance requirements (and those environmental impacts). And we consider what the impacts of a material might be on the people working or living with it—indoor air quality concerns.

The problem is that with so many different types of impacts, when we compare one product with another, we are often comparing apples to oranges. The challenge in evaluating green building materials is in balancing all the considerations.

Distant dream. The Holy Grail of the green building movement would be a database in which the life-cycle environmental impacts of different materials were fully quantified and weighted so that a builder or designer could easily see which material was better from an environmental standpoint. Though efforts are afoot along those lines—for example, the BEES software that has been developed by the National Institute of Standards and Technology (NIST)—we are not even close to fully realizing that goal. We are a long way from having a

Green Products vs. Green Building

It's important to consider the distinction between green building products and green building. One could build a green home with few materials specifically defined as green. A really compact, highly energy-efficient house on an in-fill site close to public transit, for example, would likely be defined as green even if all the materials in the house were conventional—no recycled-content decking or linoleum flooring or certified wood.

Conversely, green products can be used in dumb ways that result in buildings that are far from environmentally responsible. One could use nothing but recycled-content products but fail to pay attention to energy efficiency or where the house is built. Or one could ignore moisture control and end up with a mold farm that makes the homeowners sick. That certainly isn't green.

Green building involves more than just the selection of green products. It involves such issues as siting the home wisely, minimizing dependence on automobiles, protecting the ecosystem around the home, designing the home to benefit from passive solar energy, providing an energy-efficient building shell, and incorporating building science principles to ensure that the house will be safe and last a long time.

That said, however, substituting green products for conventional products can make the difference between a good home and a great one from an environmental standpoint.

What is Green? (continued)

truly objective way to compare the greenness of building materials, but we can still make informed decisions about selection. Let's take a more detailed look at some of the criteria that can be used to define building products as green. Through this process, you should get a sense of the tremendous variety of green building products and the many characteristics that can be used in identifying them.

Products Made With Salvaged, Recycled, or Agricultural Waste Content

The raw materials used to produce a building product—and the source of those materials—are key determinants of green.

Salvaged products. Whenever we can reuse a product instead of producing a new one from raw materials—even if those raw materials are from recycled sources—we save on resource use and energy. Many salvaged materials used in buildings (bricks, millwork, framing lumber, plumbing fixtures, and period hardware) are sold on a local or regional basis by salvage yards, but some are marketed nationally.

Products with recycled content. Recycled content is an important feature of many green products. From an environmental standpoint, post-consumer is preferable to post-industrial recycled content. "Post-consumer" means that some portion of the raw materials used in manufacturing the product was diverted from the waste stream. Plastic lumber made from recycled HDPE grocery bags and cellulose insulation made from ground-up newspapers are good examples. "Post-industrial" refers to raw materials that were waste products from industry but had never actually been in use. Iron-ore slag used in mineral wool insulation, fly ash used in concrete, and PVC scrap used to make shingles are examples of post-industrial recycled materials.

Products made from agricultural waste material. Some green building products are made from agricultural waste products. Approximately 140 million tons of straw are produced annually in North America from the harvesting of wheat, barley, rice, and other grains. In the past, most of that straw was burned in the fields, but pollution-control regulations increasingly ban that practice; using the material to produce building products is a great alternative. When it's chopped up, mixed with a binder, and compressed into panels, straw produces a superb particleboard product.

Products That Conserve Natural Resources

Aside from salvaged or recycled content, there are a number of other ways that products can contribute to the conservation of natural resources. These include products that serve a particular function while using less material than the standard solution, products that are especially durable or low-maintenance, wood products that carry Forest Stewardship Council certification, and products made from rapidly renewable resources.

Products that reduce material use. Products meeting this criterion may not be distinctly green on their own but are green because of resource efficiency benefits that they make possible. For example, drywall clips allow the elimination of corner studs, engineered stair stringers reduce lumber waste, pier foundation systems minimize concrete use, and concrete pigments can turn concrete slabs into attractive finished floors, eliminating the need for conventional finish flooring.

Products with exceptional durability or low maintenance requirements. These products are environmentally attractive because they need to be replaced less fre-

What is Green? (continued)

quently, or they require less maintenance. Fiber-cement siding and fiberglass windows, for example, can be considered green because they last longer and require less maintenance than standard products.

Certified wood products. Third-party forest certification, based on standards developed by the Forest Stewardship Council (FSC), is the best way to ensure that wood products come from well-managed forests. Wood products must go through a chain-of-custody certification process to carry an FSC stamp. While there are now other forest certification systems, including the Sustainable Forestry Initiative (SFI)—which has been strengthened significantly in the past several years—the FSC standards are still the most rigorous and the most frequently specified in the green building movement.

Rapidly renewable products. Some products are considered green because the raw materials used in producing them are replenished quickly. Natural linoleum flooring is made from linseed oil (an agricultural crop). Cork, which comes from the bark of certain oak trees, is harvested sustainably on an eight- to ten-year cycle. A new class of concrete form-release oils made from plant oils is both nontoxic and fully biodegradable. Jute, sisal, and coir are examples of natural fibers that are used in everything from wall coverings to erosion-control geotextiles. Because sunlight is generally the primary energy that produces those raw materials (via photosynthesis), they are often less energy intensive to produce than the conventional products they replace.

Products That Are Green Because of What Isn't There

Some building products are considered green because they are alternatives to conventional products that are considered hazardous.

Alternatives to conventional preservative-treated wood. CCA-treated wood, which contains both arsenic and chromium, poses a health hazard and a significant environmental risk during disposal; pentachlorophenol (penta) and creosote are considered carcinogens. Alternatives to those chemicals, such as ACQ, copper azole (Wolmanized Natural Select), and borates can thus be considered green.

Alternatives to ozone-depleting substances. Ozone-depleting substances are being eliminated through international agreement. As of this year, for example, polyisocyanurate insulation is no longer made with ozone-depleting HCFC-141b as the blowing agent. But in a few categories, the majority of products still contain or use HCFCs, including certain categories of foam insulation (extruded polystyrene and high-density spray polyurethane) and compression-cycle hvac equipment. A product can be considered green if it serves as an alternative to one of those widely used products.

Alternatives to PVC. Polyvinyl chloride (PVC), or vinyl, products contain up to 40% chlorine by weight, and if an accidental fire or improper incineration occurs, hazardous chlorinated hydrocarbons, such as dioxins, can be generated. The plasticizers used to make many PVC products soft are also considered hazardous. The debate about the relative risks of PVC has been quite heated over the past five years, with Greenpeace and other environmental groups decrying PVC as dangerous, while the plastics industry touts such products as green because of their durability and low maintenance requirements. In the green building field, the use of PVC is generally discouraged, so some products may be considered green because they are non-PVC in an application served primarily by PVC products.

What is Green? (continued)

Alternatives to mercury and other components considered hazardous. Fluorescent lamps with low mercury levels can be considered green, as can certain non-mercury lighting technologies, such as LEDs (light-emitting diodes). The absorber surfaces of solar collectors can similarly be considered green if they are made without chromium.

Natural or minimally processed products. Products that are natural or minimally processed can be green because of low energy use and low risk of chemical releases during manufacture. These can include wood products, agricultural or nonagricultural plant products, and mineral products such as natural stone and slate shingles.

Products that reduce or eliminate pesticide treatments. Periodic pesticide treatment around buildings can be a significant health and environmental hazard. The use of certain products can obviate the need for pesticide treatments, and such products are therefore considered green. Examples include physical termite barriers, borate-treated building products, and bait systems that eliminate the need for broad-based pesticide application.

Products that reduce pollution or waste from operations. Alternative wastewater disposal systems reduce groundwater pollution by decomposing organic wastes more effectively. Porous paving products and green (vegetated) roofing systems result in less stormwater runoff and thereby reduce surface water pollution and sewage treatment plant loads. Masonry fireplaces and pellet stoves burn fuel more comple-tely with fewer emissions than conven-tional fireplaces and wood stoves. Recycling bins and compost systems enable occupants to reduce their solid waste generation. All these products are green because they improve the environmental performance of building operations.

Products That Reduce Environmental Impacts During Construction, Demolition, or Renovation

Some building products achieve their environmental benefits by avoiding pollution or other negative environmental impacts during construction, renovation, or demolition. While this is a fairly small category of products, it is nonetheless important. Erosion-control products, foundation products that eliminate the need for excavation, and exterior stains that result in lower VOC emissions into the atmosphere all reduce the impact of new construction. Low-mercury fluorescent lamps reduce environmental impacts during demolition and renovation. Access flooring systems and modular carpet tiles minimize environmental impacts during renovation, because they make reconfiguration of spaces much faster and reduce waste.

Products That Save Energy or Water

The ongoing use of energy in a building is often its most significant environmental impact—and one that usually far outweighs the impacts associated with building that structure. Water consumption is becoming a more and more important consideration in buildings as droughts become more common and more severe.

Building components that reduce heating and cooling loads. Examples include structural insulated panels (SIPs), insulating concrete forms (ICFs), and high-performance windows and glazings. As these energy-saving products gain market acceptance, the performance level needed for a product to be considered green can rise. For example, while insulated-glass windows with a low-e coating may have been enough to designate a window as green several years ago, today it may take multiple low-e coatings or other green features,

What is Green? (continued)

such as more durable or recycled-content frame material.

Equipment that conserves energy. With energy-consuming equipment such as water heaters and refrigerators, it is fairly easy to identify green products — by setting a threshold for energy performance. Some green building programs identify products labeled by Energy Star as the standard for green. Other programs or directories may define tougher standards or include other criteria, such as durability, in addition to energy performance.

Renewable energy and fuel cell equipment. Equipment and products that enable us to use renewable energy instead of fossil fuels and conventional electricity are highly beneficial from an environmental standpoint and are generally considered green. Examples include solar water heaters, photovoltaic systems, and wind turbines. Fuel cells can also be considered green, even though fuel cells today nearly always use natural gas or another fossil fuel as the hydrogen source; they are considered green because emissions are lower than those of combustion-based equipment and because the use of fuel cells will help us move beyond fossil fuel dependence.

Fixtures and equipment that conserve water. Products that conserve water are often considered green, but there may be other considerations. All toilets and most showerheads, for example, now meet federal water efficiency standards, but not all of those products perform satisfactorily. A green designation may require independent evidence of superior performance.

Products That Contribute to a Safe Indoor Environment

Buildings should be safe to live and work in, and product selection is a significant determinant of indoor environment quality. Green building products that help to ensure a healthful indoor environment can be separated into several categories:

Products that release insignificant levels of pollutants. Included here are zero- and low-VOC paints, caulks, and adhesives, as well as products with very low emissions, such as nonformaldehyde-manufactured wood products. Just how low the VOC level needs to be for a given product to be considered green may vary by program and directory.

Products that block the introduction, development, or spread of indoor contaminants. Certain materials and products can be considered green because they prevent the generation or introduction of pollutants—especially biological contaminants—into occupied space. Duct mastic, for example, can block the entry of mold-laden air or insulation fibers into a duct system. Rainscreen products can help buildings dry out after wetting occurs. Entryway "track-off" systems remove pollutants from the shoes of people entering. Coated ductboard—compared with standard rigid fiberglass ductboard—prevents fiber shedding and helps control mold growth. And linoleum helps to control microbial growth because of the continuing process of linoleic acid oxidation.

Products that remove indoor pollutants. Removing stale indoor air is an important air quality practice, so a wide range of ventilation products, filters, and radon mitigation equipment can be considered green. In some product categories, other considerations may be important. Noise may be a consideration for bathroom fans, for example, because they are more likely to be used by homeowners if they're quiet. Products that warn occupants of health hazards in the building. Carbon monoxide

What is Green? (continued)

(CO) detectors and test kits for lead paint, VOCs, mold, and other potential hazards can help keep homes and workspaces safe, and so can be considered green. In some cases, performance criteria are also considered—some CO detectors are not effective, so evidence of good performance may be necessary for a green designation.

Products that improve light quality. There is a growing body of evidence that natural daylight is beneficial to our health and productivity. Products that enable us to bring daylight into a building, such as tubular skylights, can be considered green for that reason (in addition to their energy-saving benefits).

Finding Green Building Products

Selection of green building products as part of an overall green design strategy makes a great deal of sense. But finding such products can be difficult. Green building products may not be available in all building supply centers. Some are more expensive or are considered fringe products. To get your local supplier to carry green products may take some convincing. If you are committed to using FSC-certified lumber, for example, besides letting your supplier know that, you could help out by doing the research on product wholesalers your supplier could purchase from. Just a few customers asking for green products can make a huge difference—try it.

You may also find it challenging to identify which products are actually green—compared with those being marketed as green. "Greenwashing" is fairly common today, and few places exist where you can find independent verification of green claims. Specific labeling programs such as Energy Star, GreenGuard, and Green Seal can help, and there are a handful of green products directories, including our own: *GreenSpec.* Such directories can be a valuable resource.

Alex Wilson is president of Brattleboro, Vt.–based BuildingGreen, Inc., which publishes Environmental Building News *and* GreenSpec, *the leading national directory of green building products. GreenSpec carries no advertising and includes more than 1,650 products. It is available in a print edition or as part of BuildingGreen's premium web content. The fourth edition will be available in November. For more information, visit www.buildinggreen.com or call 800/861-0954.*

Materials — Rules of Thumb

👍 Consider, at a minimum, the following seven life cycle analysis criteria when selecting green materials: recycled content, waste reduction, reusability/recyclability, renewability, durability, embodied energy, and air quality impacts.

👍 Refer to *GreenSpec*, the *Guide to Resource Efficient Building Elements*, and other resources to find suppliers and get the latest information on green building materials.

👍 Consider foundation materials that have recycled waste content (e.g., flyash).

👍 Select insulation with recycled content and/or other environmental benefits (e.g, low VOCs).

👍 Select high-performance window frames and glazing to minimize the home's heating and cooling loads. Consider light pipes for additional natural lighting.

👍 Select finishes that are formaldehyde-free, have low- or no-VOC content, and are low in organic solvents.

👍 Consider SFI- or FSC-certified lumber whenever possible.

👍 Use life cycle analysis to select the greenest materials.

👍 Consider reusing excess materials, such as cutoffs, in creative ways during the construction process.

👍 Reduce and reuse material packaging as much as possible.

👍 When selecting carpeting, at the very minimum, use Carpet and Rug Institute installation guidelines and select carpets, cushions and pads, and other materials with the Carpet and Rug Institute indoor air quality label.

👍 To reduce offgassing, use tacks rather than adhesives to secure carpet.

Additional Resources

"Advanced Wall Framing," *Technology Fact Sheet*, Office of Building Technology, State and Community Programs, Energy Efficiency and Renewable Energy, U.S. Department of Energy. October 2000. 800-DOE-3732; www.eere.energy.gov/

GreenSpec: The Environmental Building News Product Directory and Guideline Specifications, Dwight Homes, Larry Strain, AIA, Alex Wilson, and Sandra Leibowitz. BuildingGreen, Inc., Brattleboro, Vermont. 1999. www.greenspec.com

Guide to Resource Efficient Building Elements, Mumma, Tracy. National Center for Appropriate Technology's Center for Resourceful Building Technology, Missoula, Montana. www.crbt.org

The Environmental Resource Guide, The American Institute of Architects (AIA). John Wiley & Sons, Inc., 1 Wiley Drive, Somerset, NJ 08875. The AIA Environmental Resource Guide provides detailed life cycle assessments of a number of construction materials. Updates are published on a biannual basis. 800-225-5945

Alternative Framing Materials in Residential Construction: Three Case Studies, NAHB Research Center. Labor and material cost analyses for SIPS, light-gauge steel, and welded-wire panels (shortcrete). Illustrated.

Environmental Building News monthly magazine. 802-257-7300;
    www.buildinggreen.com
Environmental Design and Construction magazine. 415-863-2614;
    www.edcmag.com/
Frost-Protected Shallow Foundations brochure, NAHB. Illustrated.
    800-368-5242 ext. 444; www.nahb.com/builders/frost.htm
Design Guide for Frost-Protected Shallow Foundations, 2nd Edition. NAHB
    Research Center. 800-638-8556

Web Resources

www.oit.doe.gov/steel/factsheets/steelframing.pdf
    "Development of Cost-Effective, Energy-Efficient Steel Framing." U.S.
    DOE's Energy Efficiency and Renewable Energy Office of Industrial
    Technologies. Provides information on the benefits and applications of
    steel-framed construction.
http://mts.sustainableproducts.com/standards.htm
    The Institute for Market Transformation to Sustainability: Sustainable
    Products Standards are Gaining Market Share
www.ci.austin.tx.us/greenbuilder
    Contains extensive information about insulating concrete forms.
www.eere.energy.gov/buildings/components/envelope/foundation/cfm
    Contains good information about cast-in-place concrete, concrete or
    masonry blocks, insulating concrete forms, and permanent wood foun-
    dations.
www.greenguard.org
    A global nonprofit organization with a scientific, third party board to
    establish environmental standards for indoor products and building
    materials.
www.recycle-steel.org
    Web site of the Steel Recycling Institute. Contains facts about steel recy-
    cling, educational materials, and location of steel recycling locations all
    over America.
www.steel.org
    Web site of the American Iron and Steel Institute. Contains useful infor-
    mation for builders.
www.steelframingalliance.com
    Contains useful information about steel use in homes and commercial
    buildings.
www.pathnet.org
    An excellent repository of building materials, case studies, and innova-
    tive techniques.
www.greenbuilder.com/sourcebook/
    The city of Austin's Green Building Network materials sourcebook.
www.oikos.com/products
    Oikos Green Building Product Information, formerly the Resources
    for Environmental Design Index (REDI); updated frequently and
    CSI-categorized.
www.fscus.org/certification/index.html
    Forest Stewardship Council U.S. Has information on FSC-certified
    lumber.

www.smartwood.org
SmartWood
www.greenseal.org
Green Seal
www.aboutsfi.org/sfilabel.asp
Sustainable Forestry Initiative: SFI® Labeling Program
www.epa.gov/cpg
EPA Comprehensive Procurement Guidelines (CPG). The following products list is also helpful: www.epa.gov/cpg/products.htm
www.crbt.org
The on-line version of *Guide to Resource Efficient Building Elements*, Mumma, Tracy. National Center for Appropriate Technology's Center for Resourceful Building Technology, Missoula, Montana.
www.nfrc.org
The National Fenestration Ratings Council Web site provides an industry-standard rating for use by manufacturers. Helpful window selection information is also available.
www.osbguide.com
The Structural Board Association is a group of Oriented Strand Board (OSB) manufacturers.
www.nps.gov/dsc/dsgncnstr/gpsd
National Park Service Sustainable Design and Construction Database. A free database with brief reviews of over 1,300 product listings from over 550 manufacturers.
www.wbdg.org
The Whole Building Design Guide is a comprehensive resource to a wide range of building-related design guidance, criteria, materials, and technology.
www.greenconcepts.com/greenliving/
Green Building Concepts offers green supplier listings and other green building information.
www.nrdc.org/cities/building/rwoodus.asp
The Natural Resource Defense Council's *Efficient Wood Use in Residential Construction: A Practical Guide to Saving Wood, Money, and Forests* offers an overview of OVE and other money- and wood-saving techniques. Available on-line and in print. 1998.
www.consumerenergycenter.org/homeandwork/homes/construction/index.html
The California Energy Commission's Consumer Energy Center Web site has extensive information on materials, green building, and green living.
www.bfrl.nist.gov/
The National Institute for Science and Technology's Building for WindowsEconomic and Environmental Sustainability (BEES) software helps builders identify green building products through a set of predefined life cycle criteria. Builders can choose which criteria they wish to apply.
www.concretehomes.com
Web site of the Portland Cement Association on all aspects of concrete in homes. Call (847) 966-9106 for more information.
www.coolmetalroofing.org
www.ecco.org
The Environmental Council of Concrete Organizations provides bulletins on using concrete as part of a sustainable environment. Call (800) 994-3226.

www.cement.org
> Web site of the Portland Cement Association. Contains useful information on building with concrete and using flyash and slag cement with concrete.

www.forms.org
> Web site of the Insulating Concrete Forms Association. Contains useful information on building concrete homes with ICFs. Call (847) 657-9730 for more information.

www.slagcement.org
> Web site of the Slag Cement Association. Contains useful information on using slag cement in concrete.

www.fema.gov
> Web site of the Federal Emergency Management Agency. Provides information on constructing safe rooms.

www.simplyinsulate.com
> Simply Insulate

Interactions

See the following sections for information on how Materials affect other building considerations:

Chapter 8 Operation and Maintenance

Now that you have taken the time to design and build a better home by incorporating a balanced, integrated package of green building strategies, it only makes sense to tell the home buyer all about it. Savvy buyers are looking for the same efficiencies and performance features they have come to expect in everything from cars to computers, and you are the builder who can offer those same attributes in a home. Now is the time to tell them!

Consider developing a brief, informative homeowner's manual to 1) describe the green features of the house, 2) supply information about how owners can maintain, repair, and even replace/recycle the components in their home, and 3) explain how the owner can stay comfortable and safe while minimizing energy, water, and maintenance costs. Much of this information is free from product manufacturers, local utilities and government offices, and nonprofit organizations.

The strategies below can serve as a starting point for content that can be included in a homeowner's operation and maintenance (O&M) manual. Some developers and builders have found it helpful to add listings of area parks, recreation facilities, stores, schools, government centers, etc. See the Additional Resources listing at the end of this chapter for more information.

What the Builder Can Do in the Design Process

Anticipate a maintenance schedule. All homes need maintenance, but selecting products that require periodic (rather than frequent or annual) maintenance helps the owner establish a regular schedule for upkeep. For instance, brick siding requires virtually no maintenance and can be part of a passive solar design strategy, whereas other siding options may need frequent painting or repair and would offer no passive solar or thermal mass benefits. Another example is using composite lumber for decking rather than traditional wood lumber. Whatever maintenance is anticipated for the house should be described in writing to the home buyer. Providing this information and lower maintenance products is likely to result in greater home buyer satisfaction and fewer callbacks.

Provide a homeowner's manual of green features and installed products. List the green features built into the home and the products included to make the home a safer, more comfortable place to live. Identify the benefits of each feature, so the homeowner will understand and appreciate their importance. Consider identifying how one feature relates to another (e.g., using energy-efficient lighting, appliances, and windows allowed for a smaller, more efficient air conditioner to be installed). Background information and diagrams may also be helpful.

Address storage of hazardous materials. Any cleaning supplies, paints, and other chemicals should be stored in an enclosed, vented area separated from the house. Consider providing information to the homeowner regarding the recycling and proper disposal of hazardous materials.

Provide recycling storage bins. Most millwork manufacturers include recycling centers in their cabinetry lines. It is also possible to economically install bins in existing cabinetry. Local solid waste agencies can provide guidance on the appropriate design of compost bins. The maximum cost is around $40 per linear foot. Also consider supplying a composting center for the homeowner or offering one as an option.

Provide information on HVAC operation and maintenance. Proper HVAC operation and maintenance can lead to significant savings and greater homeowner comfort. Most HVAC units should be serviced annually to maintain their efficiency. Replacing filters regularly is also important (see the Indoor Environmental Quality Tips in this chapter for more information). Consult your HVAC equipment manual for specific information.

Miscellaneous tips. Tell your home buyer about any special steps you have taken to facilitate future additions or green renovations, such as pre-plumbing for a solar hot water system or rough-ins for radon mitigation. Even telling a homeowner about your use of modular dimensions can be helpful to any future additions the homeowner may wish to make. Use nontoxic, low-VOC paint, stains, and finishes as much as possible, but especially in indoor areas. Many large paint manufacturers have added a line of low-VOC paints to their traditional product offerings. The performance and durability of these products is comparable.

What the Homeowner Can Do

Indoor environmental quality (IEQ) tips. IEQ tips range from placing doormats at all exterior doors to thorough dusting and vacuuming in order to minimize the amount of dust and dirt entering the home's ventilation system to replacing toxic solvents and cleaners with nontoxic alternatives. Selecting low-toxic cleaners safeguards health and protects the environment. Biodegradable kitchen and laundry soaps, bathroom cleaners, and other products are available in many stores and via the Web. See the References listing at the end of this chapter for additional information. To eliminate dust and allergens, homeowners should consider purchasing vacuum cleaners with microfiltration capabilities, especially high-efficiency particulate air (HEPA) filters. Another option is to consider buying pleated, electrostatic, HEPA, or electronic filters for the HVAC unit. Change air filters regularly. The interval (anywhere from 1 to 12 months) depends on the type of filter used, your local climate, and hours of HVAC operation. The EPA indicates in its publication, *Should I Have My Ducts Cleaned?*, that air ducts should not generally be cleaned in typical homes.

Integrated pest management and landscaping tips. Integrated pest management combines sanitation, physical exclusion, and mechanical controls (traps, baits, etc.) with limited, targeted pesticides. Using IPM programs often leads to fewer pests, and cleaner and healthier homes.

Collect compost made from yard waste and manure from the local parks department, department of natural resources, or other municipal agency rather than buying compost at a store.

Prune shrubs and trees enough to allow air to flow freely to an HVAC unit, but leave enough to ensure that passive solar landscaping is maintained. See Chapters 1, 2, and 5 for additional information about the effects of landscaping on energy and water conservation.

Energy and water conservation tips:

- Keep your water heater set at 120 degrees F to prevent scalding and to conserve energy. If a higher temperature for washing clothes and dishes is desired, buy appliances with booster heaters. Because of scalding risks, the hot water heater should not be set at more than 140 degrees. For every 10 degrees that you lower your hot water heater temperature, you will save an estimated 13% on your hot water heating cost.
- Service your hot water heater annually to remove sediments and other materials that lower the unit's efficiency. Another technique is to drain a gallon of water from the bottom of the hot water tank monthly.
- Set your thermostat no lower than 78 degrees in the summer and no higher than 68 degrees in the winter.
- Use a programmable thermostat to raise the summer temperature in the house by 5 degrees or more during unoccupied hours (while at work or in the evening). Conversely, lower the house's temperature in the winter. Depending on climate, turning back the household thermostat 5 degrees for even 8 hours will result in energy savings of 6% to 10%.
- Use compact fluorescent bulbs in your house. They last more than 10 times longer than traditional incandescent bulbs and use approximately 35% less energy. The replacement and energy savings more than make up for the $12-$15 purchase price.
- Set your dishwasher to the Energy Saver or Light Wash mode as often as possible. Also use the Air Dry or No Heat Dry setting.
- If you must water your lawn or garden, do so at night or before 9 a.m. to maximize the benefits to your lawn and garden and to minimize evaporation losses.
- If you have reversible ceiling fans, be sure to adjust them so they force warm air down in the winter and are moving in the opposite direction in the summer.
- Do not place furniture or other objects over HVAC registers. Do not place heat-generating appliances near the thermostat.

Miscellaneous tips. Check for termites around the exterior perimeter of the home and in the crawlspace if there is one. Environmentally friendly treatments such as termite traps and borate solution sprays are available for termite and pest control. If signs of termites are found, call a professional for inspection and treatment.

Additional Resources

Environmental Building News Product Catalog, A joint publication of E Build, Inc. and *What's Working*, 1997/98, $59. This catalog provides environmental, cost, and availability information for over 70 building materials. The catalog is set up in a three-ring binder format for easy catalog growth. As with the well-known Sweet's catalog, product literature from the manufacturer is provided, but the editors' environmental profile of the product is also provided, based on their green material selection criteria. An environmental overview of each major building material category (following CSI classifications) starts each section of the catalog.

Green Building Resource Guide, John Hermannsson AIA Architect, Taunton Press, 1997, $37.95. The *Green Building Resource Guide* lists over 600 building materials. Names and addresses of suppliers are provided, along with a brief description of the product. Cost information is provided on a relative basis, as compared to similar conventional products. The *Guide* is also available on CD-ROM.

Consumer Guide to Energy Savings, Alex Wilson and John Morrill, American Council for an Energy Efficient Economy, 2003. This book provides excellent tips on ways to conserve energy around the home. Tips on tightening up your house, heating and cooling more efficiently, lighting options, cooking, and food storage are included. Options ranging from simple things the homeowner can do at no cost to replacement of inefficient equipment is discussed.

The Green Pages: The Contract Interior Designers' Guide to Environmentally Responsible Products and Materials, Andrew Funston, Kim Plaskon Nadel, Jory Prober, New York, NY. Listings of environmentally responsible building materials from 536 manufacturers. Includes information on flooring, furnishings, fabrics, paints, appliances, lighting, and more.

The Borrower's Guide to Financing Solar Energy Systems, (DOE/GO-10098-660), Dr. Patrina Eiffert, National Renewable Energy Laboratory, Golden, CO. September 1998.

Consumers Reports has monthly and annual reports on appliances, HEPA filters and vacuums, lighting, etc.

Guide to Building Your Dream Home, Sara Lamia, Home Building Coach, Inc., September 2003.

Web Resources

www.floridaplants.com
Although oriented to Florida, this site offers numerous books on all topics from drought-tolerant plants and grasses to landscape design to pest management. In addition to printed publications, there is good information about specific trees, plants, and grasses; soil, water, and light conditions; and disease control. A useful site whether or not you live in Florida.

www.gvrd.bc.ca
Sponsored by the city of Vancouver, British Columbia, this site provides information on waste reduction with useful strategies for both the construction site and the homeowner.

www.ci.portland.or.us

> The city of Portland's Green Building Web site has an energy conservation tips page and homeowner tips page at www.ci.portland.or.us/energy/difference.htm

www.emagazine.com/

> This is the Web site for *The Environmental Magazine*. This, too, is a broad-ranging resource that includes access to information on resource-efficient home operation systems and products.

www.oikos.com/

> In addition to being a useful site for builders who are trying to locate environmentally responsible building materials, the searchable database provides homeowners with names and phone numbers of green products for use both within and outside the home. Among the types of the products listed are paving and landscaping materials, furnishings, floor coverings, paints, and stains. The library, bookstore, and back issues of *Energy Source Builder* magazine may also provide information of interest.

www.realgoods.com

> The Real Goods catalog store offers a variety of resource-efficient home products ranging from composting bins to fluorescent lighting to biodegradable cleaning agents.

www.aceee.org/consumerguide/index.htm

> American Council for an Energy Efficient Economy has lots of information on its Web site and numerous publications that educate consumers and homeowners on how to live more environmentally and economically. 202-429-0781

www.ase.org/consumer/

> The Alliance to Save Energy's consumer Web page provides vivid (and sometimes animated) energy-efficiency and conservation tips. Web links and publications are also available. 202-857-0666

www.nrdc.org/cities/living/gover.asp

> The Natural Resources Defense Council provides helpful environmental information, as well as maintenance, water efficiency, and energy tips for homeowners at www.nrdc.org/cities/living/default.asp
> Publications are also available. 212-727-2700

www.ci.austin.tx.us/greenbuilder/fs_toc.htm

> The City of Austin's Green Building Program is well-known for its builder information, but also offers valuable homeowner tips. Notable content includes fact sheets on air filters, recycling, and lead; other publications and information are also available. 512-505-3700

www.greenhome.org

> GreenHOME contains homeowner tips, as well as information on two affordable, green home construction projects.

www.eere.energy.gov/consumerinfo/forhome.html

> U.S. Department of Energy's Consumer Energy Information Web site. Contains information on appliances, HVAC, building design and maintenance, and other relevant topics.

http://Yosemite1.epa.gov/estar/homes.nsf/homepage?openform

> U.S. EPA: Energy Star for New Homes

Interactions

See the following sections for information on how Operation and Maintenance affect other building considerations:

General References

Green Building Programs

There are a growing number of green building programs across the country, many sponsored by local home builder associations and local governments, others spearheaded by nonprofit organizations, such as the local chapters of the U.S. Green Building Council. These programs provide builders and home buyers with valuable information on the benefits of green building and of buying green-built homes. Consider joining or starting a green building program in your area. The NAHB Research Center has a helpful resource called "A Guide to Developing Green Builder Programs" that can help home builders interested in program development.

In July 2002 the NAHB Research Center prepared the second edition of their Summary of Green Building Programs for the National Renewable Energy Laboratory. This document serves as a census of 26 different residential green building programs and provides detailed information about the similarities and differences among the many programs. You may find it on the Web at www.toolbase.org.

For your reference, we have included a list of the residential green building programs mentioned in the NAHB summary and have supplemented it with several other programs in various stages of development.

Green Building Programs

Arizona

Green Building Program
City of Scottsdale
(480) 312-4202; www.ci.scottsdale.az.us/greenbuilding/

Southern Arizona Green Building Alliance
The Development Center for Appropriate Technology (DCAT)
(520) 624-6628; www.dcat.net

California

Alameda County
(510) 614-1699

Chula Vista GreenStar Building Incentive Program
(619) 691-5296

California Green Builder Program
(916) 443-7933; www.thebii.org/cgbp.asp

County of Santa Barbara Innovative Building Review Program
(805) 568-2507; www.silcom.com/~sbcplan/ibdrc.html

Green Building Program
City of San Jose
Contact: Mary Tucker
(408) 277-4111; Mary.Tucker@ci.sj.ca.us
www.ci.san-jose.ca.us/esd/gb-home.htm

Colorado

Built Green Colorado
HBA of Metropolitan Denver
(303) 778-1400; www.builtgreen.org

Green Points Program
City of Boulder
(303) 441-3090; www.ci.boulder.co.us/environmental affairs/green_points/overview.html

Florida

Florida Green Building Coalition (FGBC)
(239) 263-6819; www.floridagreenbuilding.org

Georgia

EarthCraft House[SM]
Greater Atlanta Homebuilders Association
(770) 938-9900;
www.atlantahomebuilders.com/earthcraft

Green Building Programs (continued)

Hawaii

BuiltGreen
Building Industry Association of Hawaii
(808) 847-4666 x203
www.bia-hawaii.com/builtgreen/

Kansas

HBA of Greater Kansas
(816) 942-8800 x231; www.kchba.org

Maryland

Maryland Green Building Network
Contact: Sean McGuire
(410) 260-8727; smcguire@dnr.state.md.us
www.dnr.state.md.us/smartgrowth/ed/mdgbn/

Michigan

Green Built Program
HBA of Greater Grand Rapids
(616) 281-2021; www.hbaggr.com

Missouri

Heart of America Green Builders
Metropolitan Energy Center
3808 Paseo Blvd.
Kansas City, MO 64109
Contact: Robert Housch
(816) 531-7283; Rhoush@kcenergy.org
www.kcgreen.com

New Jersey

New Jersey Green Homes Office/
New Jersey Affordable Green
New Jersey Department of Community Affairs
New Jersey Green Homes Office
Division of Housing
101 South Broad St., P.O. Box 806
Trenton, NJ 08625-0800
Contact: Darren Port
(609) 292-3931; (609) 292-9798 (fax)
njgreenhome@dca.state.nj.us
www.state.nj.us/dca/dhcr/njgreenhomes.htm

New Mexico

Building America Partner Program
HBA of Central New Mexico
(505) 344-3294
www.hbacnm.com/green_builder/index.html

Green Alliance
924 Park Ave. SW
Albuquerque, NM 87102
(505) 242-6484; (505) 242-4348 (fax)
info@greenalliancenm.org
www.greenalliancenm.org

New York

New York Green Guidelines
Battery Park City
One World Financial Center
New York, NY 10281-1097
(212) 417-2000; (212) 417-2001 (fax)
www.batteryparkcity.org/guidelines.htm

Schenectady HBA Green Building
Program
Schenectady Builders and Remodelers
Association
(518) 355-0055;
www.schenectadybuilders.com

North Carolina

Western North Carolina Green Building
Council
(828) 251-5888; www.main.nc.us/wncgbc

Oregon

Earth Advantage
Portland General Electric
(888) 327-8433; www.earthadvantage.com

G/Rated Green Building
Incentive Program
City of Portland
(503) 823-7725; www.green-rated.org/

Texas

Green Building Program
City of Austin
www.ci.austin.tx.us/greenbuilder/
City of Frisco
(972) 335-5540 x145; www.ci.frisco.tx.us/
planning/greenbuilding_index.htm

Vermont

Vermont Building Green
(802) 658-6060; www.sover.net/~michaelh/bsr

Washington

Build a Better Clark
Clark County HBA
(360) 694-0933; www.cchba.com

Build a Better Kitsap
Kitsap County HBA
(360) 479-5778; www.kitsaphba.com

Built Green Seattle
Master Builders Association of King and
Snohomish Counties
(425) 451-7920; www.builtgreen.net

City of Seattle
Department of Design, Construction and
Land Use
700 Fifth Avenue, Suite 2000
Seattle, WA 98104-5070
(206) 684-7932; www.ci.seattle.wa.us/dclu

Wisconsin

Green Built Home
Wisconsin Environmental Initiative
(608) 280-0360
www.wi-ei.org/GBH/index.htm

Green Building Checklists

Some of the programs listed on the previous pages have developed checklists to help builders design and construct greener homes. Two examples are the EarthCraft House[SM] checklist from the Greater Atlanta HBA and the Vermont Building Green Program's Scorecard for Residential Certification (These resources can be found at www.southface.org/home/ech/ ech_scoring_worksheet.pdf and www.bsr-vt.org/VBG_Scorecard.pdf). Each document is included here for your reference.

The EarthCraft House[SM] checklist includes a detailed point system that helps builders choose how they will incorporate green design into their homes. The program recognizes that there are many ways to reduce pollution and the waste of natural resources when building and gives builders great flexibility in choosing the measures most valuable for their homes.

The Vermont Building Green Program is an initiative of the Vermont-based Building for Social Responsibility Group that certifies residential buildings constructed to sustainable criteria. Their Scorecard also relies on a point system and is intended to promote the healthy, durable, and resourceful construction of new residences and major renovations.

Use resources found in these and other green building checklists to create your own comprehensive plan that is appropriate to your area.

EarthCraft House^{SM} Checklist

	POINTS	SCORE	DOCUMENTATION
SITE PLANNING			
Prerequisite: Must comply with all federal, state, and local government erosion control and tree protection measures.			
erosion control site plan	2		site plan
workshop on erosion and sediment control	2		certificate
excavated topsoil protected from erosion	5		
use of redundant mulch, compost, or straw bales for erosion control	3		
grind stumps and limbs for mulch	2		
mill cleared logs	2		
registered Building *With* Trees (NAHB Program) development	15		confirmation letter
tree preservation plan	3		tree plan
utilities in tree root zones tunneled or hand dug (1 point per tree, max 5 trees)	1 per tree		
individual trees fenced at drip line (1 point per tree, max 5 trees)	1 per tree		
protected tree save area (min 25% of development or lot)	2		
tree planting (min 12 trees per acre of developed land)	4		
wildlife habitat registered with Georgia Wildlife Federation	2		confirmation letter
SITE PLANNING TOTAL			
ENERGY EFFICIENT BUILDING ENVELOPE AND SYSTEMS			
Prerequisite: Must meet or exceed the Georgia Energy Code (MEC 95 with Georgia Amendments)			
ENERGY STAR Builder may choose to certify house as ENERGY STAR OR earn a minimum of 75 points from Energy Measures	90		certificate or computer print-out
Energy Measures Must earn a minimum of 75 points. No more than 85 points under Energy Measures can be applied toward total score. Houses must meet or exceed the Georgia Energy Code.			
AIR LEAKAGE TEST			
Certify maximum 0.35 air changes/hour *OR* earn points for air sealing measures	35		test results
AIR SEALING MEASURES *maximum of 25 points*			
bottom plate of exterior walls	1		
floor penetrations between unconditioned and conditioned space	2		
bath tub and shower drain	2		
cantilevered floors sealed above supporting walls	2		
drywall sealed to bottom plate of exterior walls	1		
fireplace air sealing package (all units)	2		
drywall penetrations in exterior walls	1		
exterior wall sheathing sealed at plates, seams, and openings	4		
housewrap (unsealed at seams and openings)	1		
housewrap (sealed at plates, seams, and openings)	6		
window and door rough openings	2		
airtight IC recessed lights or no recessed lights in insulated ceilings	3		
attic access opening (pulldown stairs / scuttle hole)	1		
attic kneewall doors (weatherstripped with latch)	1		
attic kneewall has sealed exterior sheathing	3		
chases sealed and insulated	3		
ceiling drywall sealed to top plate	2		
ceiling penetrations sealed between conditioned and unconditioned space	2		
band joist between conditioned floors sealed	3		
AIR SEALING MEASURES (max of 25 applied to Air Sealing Subtotal)			
AIR SEALING SUBTOTAL			
INSULATION *Homes with multiple foundation types must use foundation type of greatest area for points*			
*slab insulation (min R4)	2		

EarthCraft House℠ Checklist (continued)

	POINTS	SCORE	DOCUMENTATION
*concrete or masonry basement walls (continuous floor to ceiling R10)	3		
*framed floor over unconditioned space (R19 in continuous contact with subfloor)	1		
*sealed , insulated crawl space walls (R8)	2		
cantilevered floor (R30)	2		
insulate fireplace chase	1		
spray applied wall insulation	4		
exterior wall stud cavities (R15)	1		
insulated headers	2		
insulated corners	2		
insulated T-walls (exterior/interior wall intersection)	2		
insulated wall sheathing (R 2.5 or greater)	2		
insulated wall sheathing (R 5 or greater)	3		
band joist insulated (R19)	2		
loose-fill attic insulation card and rulers	1		
energy heel trusses or raised top plate	2		
flat ceilings (R30)	1		
flat ceilings (R38)	2		
vaulted and tray ceilings (R25)	1		
vaulted and tray ceilings (R30)	2		
ceiling radiant heat barrier	2		
attic kneewall stud cavities (min R19)	3		
attic kneewall with non-insulated sheathing	1		
attic kneewall with insulated sheathing (R2.5)	3		
attic kneewall with insulated sheathing (R5)	5		
attic kneewall doors (R10)	1		
attic kneewall doors (R19)	2		
attic pull-down or scuttle hole (R19)	2		
INSULATION SUBTOTAL			
WINDOWS			
NFRC rated windows (max U.56)	3		NFRC label
low emissivity glazing	5		window label
inert gas-filled double glazed units (e.g. argon gas filled)	3		window label
solar heat gain coefficient (max 0.4)	3		window label
1.5-foot overhangs over 80% of windows (max 2 feet above windows)	1		
solar shade screens	3		
west facing glazing less than 2% of floor area	2		
east facing glazing less than 3% of floor area	2		
certified passive solar design (25% load reduction)	10		computer print-out
WINDOWS SUBTOTAL			
HEATING AND COOLING EQUIPMENT			
cooling equipment sized within 6000 btu/h of Manual J (all units)	5		load calc + eqmt size
heating equipment output sized within 25,000 btu/h of Manual J (all units)	2		load calc + eqmt size
measured airflow within 15% of manufacturer's specifications	3		test results
90% AFUE furnaces (75% total capacity)	6		energy guide label
SEER 12 cooling equipment (75% total capacity)	4		energy guide label
SEER 14 cooling equipment (75% total capacity)	6		energy guide label
HSPF 7.8 heat pump (75% total capacity)	4		product literature
HSPF 8.0 heat pump (75% total capacity)	6		product literature
geothermal heat pump (75% total capacity)	8		
sensible heat fraction less than or equal to 0.7 (all air conditioners)	2		
programmable thermostat (all systems)	1		

EarthCraft House^{SM} Checklist (continued)

	POINTS	SCORE	DOCUMENTATION
outdoor thermostat for heat pump	1		
cooling equipment has non-CFC and non-HCFC refrigerant	3		product literature
zone control - one system services multiple zones	5		
HEATING AND COOLING SUBTOTAL			
DUCTWORK / AIR HANDLER			
certify duct leakage less than 5%	20		test results
air handler located within conditioned space (all units)	5		
ducts located within conditioned space (min 90%)	5		
duct seams and air handler sealed with mastic (all units)	10		
duct design complies with Manual D	5		sizing calculation
airflow for each duct run measured and balanced	3		test results
no ducts in exterior walls or vaulted ceilings	3		
rigid supply trunk	2		
multiple return ducts (min 1 in each bedroom)	2		
transfer grilles	2		
interior doors with 1 inch clearance to finish floor	1		
duct trunk lines outside conditioned space insulated to R8	2		
DUCTWORK / AIR HANDLER SUBTOTAL			
ENERGY MEASURES (max of 85 applied to Building Envelope Subtotal)			
ENERGY EFFICIENT BUILDING ENVELOPE & SYSTEMS TOTAL			
ENERGY EFFICIENT LIGHTING / APPLIANCES			
indoor fluorescent fixtures (min 200 watts)	2		
recessed light fixtures are compact fluorescents	2		
automatic outdoor lighting controls (e.g. motion sensor)	2		
high efficiency exterior lighting	2		product literature
energy efficient dishwasher	1		product label
energy efficient refrigerator	2		product label
no garbage disposal	1		
ENERGY EFFICIENT LIGHTING / APPLIANCES TOTAL			
RESOURCE EFFICIENT DESIGN			
house smaller than 2100 square feet	2		
floor plan adheres to 2-ft dimensions	2		
interior living space adheres to 2-ft dimensions	1		
floor joists @ 24-in. centers (all floors)	5		
floor joists @ 19.2-in. centers (all floors)	3		
non-load bearing wall studs @ 24-in. centers	2		
all wall studs @ 24-in. centers	3		
window rough openings eliminate jack stud	2		
non-structural headers in non-load bearing walls	2		
single top plate with stacked framing	3		
2-stud corners with drywall clips or alternative framing	3		
T-walls with drywall clips or alternative framing	3		
RESOURCE EFFICIENT DESIGN TOTAL			
RESOURCE EFFICIENT BUILDING MATERIALS			
RECYCLED AND NATURAL CONTENT MATERIALS			
concrete with fly ash (min 25% fly ash)	3		content print-out
recycled concrete used as aggregate	1		letter
insulation (min 25% recycled)	1		product literature
reclaimed wood flooring	1		letter

EarthCraft House℠ Checklist (continued)

	POINTS	SCORE	DOCUMENTATION
recycled content tiles (min 30% recycled)	1		product literature
cork or bamboo flooring	1		
carpet (min 50% recycled)	1		product literature
carpet pad (min 50% recycled)	1		
outdoor decking and porches (min 40% recycled)	2		
air conditioner condensing unit pad (min 50% recycled)	1		
RECYCLED AND NATURAL CONTENT MATERIALS SUBTOTAL			
ADVANCED PRODUCTS			
engineered floor framing (all floors)	4		
engineered roof framing	2		
OSB roof decking	1		
all beams are steel, engineered wood, or trusses	1		
all headers are steel or engineered wood	1		
engineered wall framing (25% of studs)	1		
engineered wall framing (80% of studs)	2		
engineered interior trim	1		
engineered exterior trim including soffit, fascia, and trim	1		
steel interior wall framing	1		
Structural Insulated Panels (exterior walls)	5		
Structural Insulated Panels (roof)	3		
Precast Autoclaved Aerated Concrete	5		
Insulated Concrete Forms	5		
ADVANCED PRODUCTS SUBTOTAL			
DURABILITY			
roofing (min 25-year warranty)	1		warranty
roofing (min 30-year warranty)	2		warranty
roofing (min 40-year warranty)	3		warranty
light roof color (tile or metal)	2		
roof drip edge	1		
exterior cladding (min 3 sides with 40-year warranty or masonry)	1		
walls covered with builder paper or housewrap (drainage plane)	1		
siding with vented rain screen	1		
back-primed siding and trim	1		
10 year warranty on all insulated glazing	1		warranty
window and door head flashing	1		
window and door pan & side flashing	1		
continuous foundation termite flashing	1		
roof gutters that discharge water 5 feet away from foundation	1		
covered entry ways (all doors)	2		
DURABILITY SUBTOTAL			
RESOURCE EFFICIENT BUILDING MATERIALS TOTAL			
WASTE MANAGEMENT			
Prerequisite: No construction materials shall be burned or buried on job site or anywhere but in a state-approved landfill.			
WASTE MANAGEMENT PRACTICES			
job site framing plan with cut list	1		frame plan + cut list
job site framing plan with locations of studs, joists, and roof structure with cut list	10		frame plan + cut list
central cut area	3		
donation of excess materials or re-use (min $500/job)	1		letter
WASTE MANAGEMENT PRACTICES SUBTOTAL			
RECYCLE CONSTRUCTION WASTE			

EarthCraft House℠ Checklist (continued)

	POINTS	SCORE	DOCUMENTATION
posted job site waste management plan - recycle 75% of 3 materials	5		management plan
wood	3		
cardboard	1		
metal	1		
drywall (recycle or grind and spread on site)	3		
plastics	1		
shingles	1		
RECYCLE CONSTRUCTION WASTE SUBTOTAL			
WASTE MANAGEMENT TOTAL			
INDOOR AIR QUALITY			
Prerequisite: No unvented combustion fireplaces or space heaters are permitted.			
COMBUSTION SAFETY			
detached garage	5		
attached garage - seal bottom plate and penetrations to conditioned space	4		
attached garage - exhaust fan controlled by motion sensor or timer	2		
direct vent, sealed combustion fireplace (all units)	3		
furnace combustion closet isolated from conditioned area (all units)	4		
water heater combustion closet isolated or power vented	4		
carbon monoxide detector (one per floor required)	4		
backdraft depressurization test	4		test results
COMBUSTION SAFETY SUBTOTAL			
MOISTURE CONTROL			
foundation drain on top of footing	1		
foundation drain at outside perimeter edge of footing	2		
drainage board for below grade walls	4		
gravel bed beneath slab	3		
vapor barrier beneath slab(above gravel) and in crawl space	2		
capillary break between foundation and framing	1		
MOISTURE CONTROL SUBTOTAL			
VENTILATION			
radon/soil gas vent system	3		
radon test of home prior to occupancy	2		
Energy Star bath fans (all units)	3		product literature
automatic tub/shower room fan controls (e.g. timer)	1		
kitchen range hood or downdraft vented to exterior	3		
ceiling fans (minimum of 3 fans)	1		
whole house fan	2		
controlled house ventilation (0.35 ACH)	4		
dehumidification system	3		
vented garage storage room	1		
no power roof vents	1		
outside air intake without damper	2		
outside air intake with dampers	3		
VENTILATION SUBTOTAL			
MATERIALS			
subfloor urea-formaldehyde free	1		product literature
all cabinets, shelves, and countertops urea formaldehyde free	1		product literature
all surfaces of particle board in house sealed with water-based sealant	1		
low VOC paints (less than 250 g/L)	1		product literature
low VOC stains and finishes on wood floors	1		product literature

EarthCraft House℠ Checklist (continued)

	POINTS	SCORE	DOCUMENTATION
low VOC sealents and adhesives (less than 250 g/L)	1		product literature
low VOC carpet certified by the Carpet & Rug Institute	1		product literature
alternative termite treatment	2		
outdoor structures made from non-CCA pressure treated lumber	1		product literature
central vacuum system with outside collection receptacle	1		
filter / air cleaner with minimum 30% dust spot efficiency (e.g. pleated filter)	2		
ducts protected until construction is completed	2		
MATERIALS SUBTOTAL			
INDOOR AIR QUALITY TOTAL			
WATER - INDOOR			
Prerequisite: All fixtures must meet National Energy Policy Act standards for low flow.			
water filter (NSF certified)	1		product literature
high efficiency clothes washer	2		product label
pressure reducing valve	1		
high efficiency showerheads (max 2.25 gal/min)	1		product literature
high efficiency bathroom faucets (max 2.25 gal/min)	1		product literature
high efficiency kitchen faucets (max 2.25 gal/min)	1		product literature
high efficiency toilets (max 1.45 gal/min)	1		product literature
hot water demand re-circulation	1		
shower drain heat recovery device	2		
high efficiency water heater (min Energy Factor: gas 0.62 electric 0.92)	2		energy guide label
water heater tank insulation	1		
water heater pipe insulation on first two feet of pipe	1		
heat traps on water heater	1		
heat recovery water heating	1		
solar domestic water heating	3		
heat pump water heater	2		
WATER - INDOOR TOTAL			
WATER - OUTDOORS			
HBA WATER SMART program	5		certificate
xeriscape guidebook given to homeowner	1		resource
xeriscape plan provided to homeowner	4		xeriscape plan
xeriscape installed	15		
timer on hose bibs or irrigation system	1		
drip irrigation system	2		

EarthCraft House^SM Checklist (continued)

	POINTS	SCORE	DOCUMENTATION
greywater irrigation	3		
rainwater harvest system	3		
permeable pavement driveway / parking area	2		
WATER - OUTDOORS TOTAL			
HOMEBUYER EDUCATION			
guaranteed energy bills	15		energy bill guarantee
review energy operations with homeowner	1		
review irrigation system operations with homeowner	2		
built-in recycling center	2		
local recycling contact	1		
household hazardous waste resources	1		
environmental features checklist for walk through	4		
HOMEBUYER EDUCATION TOTAL			
BUILDER OPERATIONS			
builder commits 80% of total homes to EarthCraft House standards	4		
markets EarthCraft House program	2		
environmental checklist provided to all subcontractors	1		
Certified Professional Home Builder	3		certificate
uses HBA Homeowner Handbook for warranty standards	2		
BUILDER OPERATIONS TOTAL			
BONUS POINTS			
site located within 1/4 mile of mass transit	5		
sidewalk connects house to business district (max 2 miles)	5		
brownfield site	5		
solar electric system	25		
alternative fuel vehicles: electric charging station or natural gas pump	5		
home safety certification	1		
accessibility certification	2		
American Lung Association Health House	5		
exceeds Energy Star (1 point for each 1%) max 5 points			
Innovation points - Builder submits specifications for innovative products or design features to qualify for additional points			
BONUS POINTS TOTAL			

EarthCraft House℠ Checklist (continued)

	POINTS	SCORE	DOCUMENTATION
	MIN		
EARTHCRAFT HOUSE TOTALS			
SITE PLANNING	0		
ENERGY EFFICIENT BUILDING ENVELOPE AND SYSTEMS	75		
ENERGY EFFICIENT LIGHTING / APPLIANCES	0		
RESOURCE EFFICIENT DESIGN	0		
RESOURCE EFFICIENT BUILDING MATERIALS	0		
WASTE MANAGEMENT	0		
INDOOR AIR QUALITY	0		
WATER - INDOOR	0		
WATER - OUTDOORS	0		
HOMEBUYER EDUCATION	0		
BUILDER OPERATIONS	0		
BONUS POINTS	0		
GRAND TOTAL	150		

Vermont Building Green Scorecard

The Vermont Building Green (VBG) Scorecard is the intellectual property of Building for Social Responsibility (BSR) and is proprietary information. Any use or reproduction of the Scorecard, except for one-time individual use, is forbidden without the express written permission of BSR. Use of the Scorecard, in any form, by programs, organizations, businesses, governmental agencies, etc. must be first approved by BSR. At the same time, BSR welcomes any and all input that helps improve the Scorecard. BSR can be contacted at buildingforsocialresponsibility@yahoo.com.

Vermont Building Green Scorecard (continued)

Category	Strategy	Approach	Points
1. SITING AND LAND USE			
1)		**Location: Choose location to reduce the dependence on automobiles**	
	a	Locate site within 3 miles of public transport stop. (within 1 mile - 2 pts., 1/4 mile - 3 pts.)	1
	b	Locate within 3 miles of public school. (1 mile - 2 pts., 1/4 mile - 3 pts.)	1
	c	Locate within 3 miles of a food store. (1 mile - 2 pts., 1/4 mile - 3 pts.)	1
	d	Provision for pedestrians, including pathways, bicycle routes and bicycle storage facilities.	2
	e	In-fill development – locate housing in empty lots in an existing neighborhood.	3
	f	Build on a brownfield site or previously built-on site. (Brownfield: previously occupied site where ecosystems are damaged, requiring at least some landscape restoration)	3
	g	Install approach that meets the goal of this strategy not listed above (upon documentation and submission to VBG Program Committee).	TBD
2)		**Optimize land use to minimize damage to the environment and, where possible improve the environment.**	
	a	Do not build on currently usable prime agricultural land.	Required
	b	Do not build on wetlands or sensitive wildlife habitat. (as defined by the state of Vermont)	Required
	c	Protect against erosion during construction and landscaping.	Required
	d	Do not build in the 100 year flood plain.	Required
	e	Provide and implement responsible storm water management plan for site, including: Avoid storm sewering where possible; Minimize impervious ground coverings and reduce roadway widths & lengths; Provide vegetative swales for storm water infiltration.	3
	f	Preserve existing trees and vegetation, except within 30' of buildings, except for driveway, solar access, areas cleared for food production and as required for grading for drainage requirements.	3
	g	Protect existing ecosystems during construction through the use of snow fencing and other access barriers.	2
	h	Design roadways and parking to not intrude upon open space.	2
	i	Restore damaged ecosystems.	3
	j	Preserve topsoil on site. Restore after construction.	2
	k	Use trees cut from site in house construction	2
	l	Grind stumps and limbs for mulch.	1
	m	Cut and reserve non-millable hardwood for firewood.	1
	n	No trenching, covering or compacting tree root zones in building and site-work areas.	1
	o	Preserve wildlife habitat and wildlife corridors.	2
	p	Permeable pavement driveway/parking.	2

Vermont Building Green Scorecard (continued)

q		Integrate public transportation access into site plan.	2
r		Mowed lawn and landscaping area total less than 1/4 acre.	2
s		Lawn species selected to minimize mowing/lawn maintenance.	2
t		Landscape with at least 75% native species. One additional point for 100%.	2
u		Landscape with northern hardy edible plants/trees.	2
v		Landscape with wildlife habitat enhancing species.	1
w		Install approach that meets the goal of this strategy not listed above (upon documentation and submission to VBG Program Committee).	TBD
3)		**Community: Promote community and security through site and building design.**	
a		Creation of conservation and property sale restrictions to preserve sustainable intent.	3
b		Minimize visual impact of new structures from open fields, mountains and water bodies.	2
c		Developments of more than one home must utilize at least three (3) of the following approaches in order to receive these points:	
	i	Porches oriented toward neighbors or public right of way.	2
	ii	Minimize front yard set-back.	2
	iii	Cluster buildings in order to preserve land or foster community.	3
	iv	Indoor spaces common to multiple units.	2
	v	Outdoor spaces common to multiple units.	2
	vi	Neighborhood parks.	2
	vii	Creation of deed-protected affordable housing lots.	2
d		Unit in co-housing development.	3
e		Unit in multifamily housing development.	3
f		Install approach that meets the goal of this strategy not listed above (upon documentation and submission to VBG Program Committee).	TBD

2. BUILDING DESIGN

1)		**Efficient building design**	
a		Incremental design (e.g. building only what is needed at the present with documented provisions to expand to meet growing needs).	2
b		Flexibility of design (e.g. adaptable for changing use in future such as stubbing plumbing for additional bathroom, running hardwood floors under partitions for changing room layout, etc.) Point per documented strategy, max of 3 points.	1
c		Multiple use areas (e.g. desk area with provisions for computer center/sewing space/work space or great room area for living/dining/recreation) (Point per area, maximum of 3 pts.)	1
d		Novel storage (e.g. using dead areas like knee walls for storage). (Point per area, maximum of 3 pts.)	1
e		Cold storage room cooled by outside air (i.e., root cellar).	2
f		Building without full basement, shallow frost protected slab on grade.	2
g		Earth-sheltered house (significant portion of walls and roof are earth sheltered)	3
h		Earth-bermed house (significant portion of walls are earth bermed).	2
I		Airlock at least 50% of exterior entrances. Additional point for 100%.	1
j		Mudroom.	1
k		No garage	3
l		Location of unheated garage on the north and winter windward sides.	2
m		Location of utility spaces on the north and winter windward sides.	1
n		Building orientated within 15 degrees of true south, with the long axis of the building east/west.	3
o		Improve day lighting with more than 60% of all glass openings higher than mid-height of the average interior wall.	2
p		Restrict heat loss by limiting skylight/monitor area to no more than 6% of the total net floor area of the room in which it is located.	2
q		Unobstructed south facing roof for future PV or solar hot water. Pitch within 10% of latitude (35-45 degrees).	2
r		Automatically controlled high R-Value insulating window shades and shutters.	2
s		Chimney within building envelope.	1
t		Inclusion of comprehensive green criteria in project construction document specifications.	3
u		Inclusion of green and energy conserving details and assembly instructions in project construction document drawings and/or specifications.	3
v		Efficient circulation design (circulation areas less than 10% of gross square footage).	2
w		Dedicated business office in home. (2 points per area, maximum 4 pts.)	2
x		Install approach that meets the goal of this strategy not listed above (upon documentation and submission to VBG Program Committee).	TBD

Vermont Building Green Scorecard (continued)

3. QUALITY/DURABILITY			
1)		**Choose quality materials and details for minimum maintenance requirements.**	
	a	Install materials with proper detailing to control degradation from sun, heat and moisture, including: Wood>8"above soil; Roof/wall flashing with siding cut 2" above roofing; minimum 10" overhang size at eaves with a sloped roof.	Required
	b	Minimum 25-year expected lifetime roof warranty.	Required
	c	10 year warranty on vertical insulated glass.	Required
	d	Reduced ice dams: No non-airtight recessed light fixtures in insulated flat ceilings; no non-airtight recessed fixtures in insulated cathedral ceilings.	Required
	e	Reduced ice dams: At least R-30 attic/roof-slope insulation R-value extending over outside of exterior walls.	Required
	f	Effective flashing on all rough openings, including membrane flashing on bottom of all rough openings for windows and doors using adhesives compatible with drainage plane materials and window and door head casing flashing.	Required
	g	Detail deck to house connection to shed water away from house.	Required
	h	20 year insulated glass warranty.	2
	i	Beyond 25 year roofing warranty. (an additional 1-point for each five year increase in warranty or expected life time)	1
	j	Reduced ice dams: R-38 attic/roof-slope insulation R-value extending over outside of exterior walls.	1
	l	Minimum 10" gable overhangs over wall siding.	1
	m	Stainless steel fasteners. 1 point for each of the following applications:	
	i	Siding.	1
	ii	Trim.	1
	iii	Decking.	1
	n	40 year siding warranty or expected life time.	1
	o	50 year siding warranty or expected life time.	2
	p	Brick or stone siding 90% (or more).	3
	q	Exterior siding/veneer built over vented drainage plane.	3
	r	If wood, six sides of siding primed.	3
	s	Crushed stone or other material below roof drip line to minimize splash on siding.	2
	t	Provide detail drawing and/or photo documentation of roof assembly identifying materials used to ensure roof assembly sheds exterior moisture effectively and is protected from degradation due to interior heat and moisture migration.	3
	u	Fiberglass composite framed windows.	3
	v	Clad windows.	1
	w	Entryway protection by roof overhang (minimum 3 feet).	1
	x	Plan landscaping so that mature plantings will be at least 24" from house.	1
	y	Install all insulated, non-wood exterior doors.	1
	z	At grade stone, masonry or concrete patio in place of wood.	3
	aa	Install approach that meets the goal of this strategy not listed above (upon documentation and submission to VBG Program Committee).	TBD

4. ENERGY USE			
1)		**Envelope and Systems: Implement a comprehensive approach to energy-efficient design.**	
	a	Certified as ENERGY STAR® Home (5-Stars or 86 points on the Home Energy Rating System scale) for new construction; 4-Stars Plus (83 points) for existing homes.	Required
	b	Mechanical equipment must be accessible for service, including AC condensate drain pan and trap.	Required
		Ducted Heating and/or Cooling Systems:	
	c	Installation of all heating and cooling ducts and mechanical equipment within the building envelope or ducting tested to be less than 1% leakage to outside.	Required
	d	Air conditioning equipment sized within 10% or next available size of ACCA Manual J.	Required
	e	Forced air heating/cooling ductwork for primary space conditioning system complies with ACCA Manual D design criteria.	Required
	f	If necessary, any ducts that run in outside walls must have at least R-7.5 between ducts and outside.	Required
	g	Central air conditioning refrigerant charge and air flow documented to be within 10% of manufacturer recommendation.	Required
	h	Air filter housings must be air-tight to prevent bypass or leakage.	Required
	i	Air flow for each register measured and complies with Manual D design.	2
	j	Returns OR transfer grill in each room with closeable door.	2

Vermont Building Green Scorecard (continued)

k	More than one return per zone.	1
Hydronic Heating Systems:		
l	Hydronic distribution system located 100% within house envelope.	2
m	Hydronic distribution system pipes insulated where they run through unconditioned (i.e. no thermostat) spaces (e.g. basements, crawlspaces, etc.).	1
n	Hydronic distribution system designed and sized to match room-by-room loads (submit sizing plan).	2
o	Hydronic boiler with less than 4 gallons water content and/or "low mass".	2
p	Boiler controls set up to "cold start" (i.e. does not maintain boiler water temperature 24/7, but allowed to drift down).	2
q	Modulating aquastat/outdoor temperature sensing controls to adjust circulating boiler water.	2
Other Energy Saving Strategies:		
r	Points per added Home Energy Rating point above 5-Star 86 point Rating for new and above 83 points for existing homes (use conventional rounding up or down to nearest whole Rating point).	2
s	No air conditioning installed.	3
t	Points for each heating zone beyond one (excludes semi-conditioned basement).	1
u	Shade with trees at least 50% of all sidewalks, roadways, and parking areas within 50' of the house.	1
v	Planted (or building sited with) windbreak on north or northwest.	2
w	Preserve or plant new shade trees and vegetation for shading west sides of building.	2
x	Additional interior mass by adding second layer of (minimal 1/2") gypsum wall board.	3
y	Trellises to shade west side glass.	1
z	Low-solar admittance glass on west, whole window SHGC <.40.	2
aa	Awnings or overhang designed to reduce summer heat gain.	1
bb	Locate hot water heater within 20 feet pipe run of all showers/baths and kitchen.	2
cc	Whole house cooling/'night flushing' fan with tight insulated winter closure system.	2
dd	Install approach that meets the goal of this strategy not listed above (upon documentation and submission to VBG Program Committee).	TBD

2)	**Efficient Lighting and Appliances**	
a	At least 10 (6 in homes <1,500 sq.ft) ENERGY STAR® or Vermont ENERGY STAR® Homes (VESH) qualified fluorescent light fixtures in VESH qualified high use locations [High Use = 2 or more hours/ average daily use].	Required
b	ENERGY STAR® or equivalent Refrigerator. (See www.energystar.gov).	Required
c	ENERGY STAR® or equivalent Dishwasher, if dishwasher installed. (See www.energystar.gov).	Required
d	ENERGY STAR® or equivalent Clothes washing machine, if washing machine installed. (See www.energystar.gov).	Required
Lighting:		
e	Per fixture of high-use ENERGY STAR® or equivalent lighting fixtures beyond required fixtures (maximum 10 points).	2
f	Per hard-wired incandescent fixture with ENERGY STAR® screw-in bulbs installed (maximum 10 points).	1
g	Use a comprehensive approach to high-quality lighting design – points for lighting design submitted.	3
h	Light pollution minimized through avoiding no direct beam illumination beyond visible property lines.	1
i	Common spaces such as hallways that would otherwise require 24 hour lighting (e.g. multi-family) utilize day lighting and automatic lighting controls.	2
j	Interior motion sensor with photocell. (1 point per fixture, maximum 3 points)	1
k	Exterior motion sensor with photocell. (1 point per fixture, maximum 2 points)	1
Appliances:		
l	Other ENERGY STAR® appliances (See www.energystar.gov). (1 point per appliance)	1
m	Gas-fired clothes dryers with electronic ignition, if dryer hookup provided.	1
n	Install a clothesline – 2 points each for indoor and outdoor permanent clotheslines. (max. 4 points)	2
o	Install approach that meets the goal of this strategy not listed above (upon documentation and submission to VBG Program Committee).	TBD

3)	**Sustainable Equipment**	
a	No electric resistance space heat.	Required

Vermont Building Green Scorecard (continued)

b	No electric resistance domestic hot water systems except as solar back-up (electric back-up consumption may not exceed 2,000 kWh/yr).	Required
c	EPA, Canadian or MHA certified wood burning appliance as a primary heat source with an output capacity greater than 50% of Manual J or IBR heat load.	3
d	EPA, Canadian or MHA certified wood burning appliance as an auxiliary heat source with an output capacity less than 50% of Manual J or IBR heat load.	1
e	Drain heat-recovery system (I.e. "GFX" or "Drain Gain") 2 points per system.	2
f	Grey water heat recovery system.	2
g	Rough-in of plumbing and wiring and roof orientation for future solar hot water or photovoltaics.	2
h	Solar water heating.	2
i	Points per peak Watt photovoltaics and/or rated Watt of wind or hydro site generated power installed.	0.01
j	Points per peak Watt photovoltaics and/or rated Watt of wind or hydro site generated power with grid connection (bonus).	0.02
k	Intake air solar preheating system (e.g. Solarwall, etc.).	2
l	On-site fuel cell.	3
m	On-site fuel cell powered by a renewable fuel source (additive with above).	3
n	On-site district heating system.	3
o	On-site district district heating system powered by a renewable fuel source (additive with above).	3
p	On-site co-generation.	3
q	On-site co-generation powered by a renewable fuel source (additive with above).	3
r	Electric vehicle recharging station.	2
s	HFC refrigerant in air conditioning system.	1
t	Install approach that meets the goal of this strategy not listed above (upon documentation and submission to VBG Program Committee).	TBD

5. RESOURCE IMPACTS

1)   Resource-efficient and environmentally responsible materials

a	Only tropical wood that is third-party certified sustainably harvested (includes luan plywood).	Required
b	Use only ACQ wood where treated wood is needed.	Required
c	No old-growth wood, (except reused) including clear redwood, Western cedar, Douglas Fir.	3
d	No CFCs or HCFCs in building materials or in manufacturing process (excluding refrigerants in refrigerators or air conditioning systems).	3
e	2 points for each 5% of total value of materials in the building products made with salvaged, recycled or waste-stream content. Examples include re-habilitation of a used house, used doors or cabinets, cellulose insulation, straw-based particle-board, fly-ash-content concrete, re-sawn salvaged wood, recycled plastic lumber, etc.	2
f	Per 10% of the value ($) of solid structural wood that is third-party certified as sustainably harvested.	2
g	Per 10% of the value ($) of non-solid structural wood that is third-party certified as sustainably harvested.	2
h	Per 5% fly ash type "C" or type "F" in concrete .	1
i	Non-petroleum concrete form release oil.	1
j	Engineered wood or steel beams (90% minimum).	1
k	Engineered wood headers (90% minimum).	1
l	Engineered floor framing (90% minimum).	2
m	Engineered roof framing (90% minimum).	2
n	Engineered wall framing (90% minimum).	2
o	Steel interior wall studs (90% minimum).	2
p	OSB (without added urea formaldehyde adhesive) roof decking .	1
q	OSB (without added urea formaldehyde adhesive) floor decking.	1
r	OSB (without added urea formaldehyde adhesive) wall sheathing.	1
s	Interior finger-jointed trim, minimum of 50%.	2
t	Agricultural by-product based panels.	1
u	Straw bale, earth sheltered or other natural mass material system (not including log) construction: per 20% of component (i.e. walls) construction.	2
v	Cellulose insulation in walls.	3
w	Cellulose insulation in roof/ceilings.	3
x	Recycled mineral fiber insulation.	2
y	100% recycled fiberglass insulation with larger (less toxic) fibers.	2

Vermont Building Green Scorecard (continued)

	z	Structural Insulated Panel (SIP) construction: per 20% of component (i.e.. Walls/roof) construction.	1
	aa	Tile - minimum 50% recycled content of tiles (1 point per 33% of total tiled area).	1
	bb	Carpet - minimum 50% recycled content of carpet (1 point per 33% of total carpeted area).	1
	cc	Carpet pad - minimum 50% recycled content of carpet pad (1 point per 33% of total carpeted area).	1
	dd	Non-wood outdoor decking - minimum 50% recycled content of non-wood decking (1 point per 33% of total decking area).	1
	ee	Recycled content gypsum board.	3
	ff	Natural-based product for finish siding (includes wood, masonry, fiber cement, stucco).	2
	gg	Natural-based product for finish trim (includes wood, masonry, fiber cement, stucco).	2
	hh	Exposed concrete floor with sealer and optional stain finish in living areas.	1
	ii	Zero Ozone depleting spray foam insulation - all walls	2
	jj	Zero Ozone depleting spray foam insulation - all ceilings	2
	kk	No PVC piping.	2
	Use of local or regional materials:		
	ll	Points per 10% of value of solid structural wood that is regionally sourced (3 points within 200 miles, 2 points within 400 miles, 1 point within 800 miles), excluding concrete.	1
	m m	Points per 20% of value of non-structural wood that is regionally sourced (3 points within 200 miles, 2 points within 400 miles, 1 point within 800 miles), excluding concrete.	1
	nn	Points per 10% of value of non-wood materials that are regionally sourced (3 points within 200 miles, 2 points within 400 miles, 1 point within 800 miles), excluding concrete.	1
	oo	Install approach that meets the goal of this strategy not listed above (upon documentation and submission to VBG Program Committee).	TBD
2)	**Reduce, Re-Use and Recycle**		
	Minimize waste and encourage diversion of waste for re-use and recycling during the construction process:		
	Definitions: *Re-use*: to separate for later re-use by the builder or by others. *Recycling*: to separate and transport material to a central location for re-manufacturing by others		
	a	Create and implement a plan for construction to provide for the efficient separation of materials which are reusable or recyclable, including separate containers, covered where required, for the following: wood, cardboard, metal, drywall (grind or recycle on site) plastics, asphalt shingles, other materials for re-use for which local infrastructure exists (comply with your local solid waste management plan	Required
	b	Optimize material use by designing for standard ceiling heights, wall lengths and building dimensions in 2 foot increments.	3
	c	Avoid waste from structural over-design. (Points for submitting engineer's calculations showing beam sizing)	2
	Use typical OVE (Optimal Value Engineering) framing details:		
	d	24" center studs *(OVE)*.	2
	e	Eliminate jack studs in rough openings *(OVE)*.	2
	f	Non-structural headers in non-load-bearing walls *(OVE)*.	2
	g	Single top plate with stacked framing *(OVE)*.	2
	h	2-stud corners with drywall clips or plywood drywall nailers *(OVE)*.	2
	i	Job-site framing plan in architectural plan set and cut list on site.	3
	j	Donate excess and re-usable materials for re-use.	2
	k	Insulated concrete forms for foundation which stay in place or walls using at least 50% recycled content.	3
	Countertops:		
	i	Install re-used countertops (minimum 75% of countertop area).	2
	ii	Install countertops made from recycled materials (minimum 75% of countertop area).	1
	iii	Install re-usable countertops (minimum 75% of countertop area).	1
	iv	Install recyclable countertops (minimum 75% of countertop area).	1
	l	Install approach that meets the goal of this strategy not listed above (upon documentation and submission to VBG Program Committee).	TBD
3)	**Encourage diversion of waste for recycling during occupancy**		
	a	Provide space for recycling containers at convenient location for storage of recyclables (Define space)	Required
	b	Provide composting and/or worm bins on site.	1
	c	Built-in kitchen recycling center.	1

Vermont Building Green Scorecard (continued)

d		Install approach that meets the goal of this strategy not listed above (upon documentation and submission to VBG Program Committee).	TBD

4)	**Water efficiency**		
	a	Landscaping that requires no irrigation system once mature.	3
	b	Install 2.0 gpm shower heads (all).	1
	c	Install 1.5 gpm shower heads (all).	2
	d	Install high quality water-efficient toilet using 1.0 gallon or less per flush (all).	2
	e	Separate and re-use gray water.	3
	f	Install composting toilet.	3
	g	High-efficiency drip automatic irrigation system for gardens.	1
	h	Collect and use rainwater for garden use.	1
	i	Collect and use rainwater for potable use.	3
	j	Innovative wastewater technology (constructed wetland, etc.).	3
	k	Install approach that meets the goal of this strategy not listed above (upon documentation and submission to VBG Program Committee).	TBD

6. OCCUPANT HEALTH/INDOOR AIR QUALITY			
		This includes using materials and systems that minimize pollutant introduction into the home as well as the use of ventilation to dilute and remove any pollutants that are introduced. It also includes health and safety of builders and workers that produce materials.	
1)	**Minimize sources of pollutants**		
	a	All combustion appliances (excluding gas ovens/ranges) must be vented to the outside and either sealed-combustion, direct vent, power-vented, induced draft, or aerodynamically de-coupled from the indoor air.	Required
	b	All solid fuel heating and water heating appliances (including fireplaces) must have tight-fitting doors and dedicated outside combustion air. Non-closed combustion systems must be aerodynamically de-coupled from the indoor air	Required
	c	Garages to be 100% air sealed from adjacent living spaces.	Required
	d	Furnaces in garage must have completely sealed duct, cabinet and filter systems.	Required
	e	Provide smoke detectors per code (hardwired with battery backup).	Required
	f	Provide carbon monoxide detectors if there is any open combustion equipment (gas range) or an attached garage (hardwired with battery backup).	Required
	g	Non-mercury thermostats.	Required
	h	Foundation continuous footing drain with stone covered with filter fabric, drained to daylight or if necessary to drain to the interior, use a sealed sump pump system. (Drainage system not required in pure sand.)	Required
	i	Basement foundation walls use porous backfill material.	Required
	j	Provide continuous crushed stone under footings or provide pipe through footing for drainage of any accumulated water under slab to drainage.	Required
	k	Vapor retarder (poly or rigid insulation) directly under slab.	Required
	l	Exterior of below grade foundation damp proofed.	Required
	m	Crawlspaces not vented; crawlspace walls insulated; crawlspace floor with complete, continuous sealed vapor retarder, also sealed to walls. (Must complete all approaches.)	Required
	n	Provide swales to divert surface water from hillsides.	Required
	o	No carpet in kitchens, bathrooms, spa areas, or within 3' of entry doors.	Required
	p	Carpet installed on slab on grade or on concrete basement floor, must have: minimum R-10 continuous insulation under slab and minimum R-5 slab edge insulation break at foundation wall intersection and R-10 slab edge insulation outward of any walk-out slab edge	Required
	q	No adhesives for carpet attachments unless zero VOC (100 grams per liter or less).	Required
	r	Insulate and sheath using rigid draft stop, and air seal bathroom exterior walls behind showers and tubs before installing showers, tubs and spas.	Required
	s	Seal top of footing prior to pouring foundation wall OR provide continuous crushed stone base under footings.	1
	t	Exterior of below grade building envelope sealed with moisture barrier assembly system (e.g. Rub-R-Wall system, etc.).	3
	u	Slope top of backfill to achieve settled slope of 1" per foot to at least 3' from foundation. Pitch final grading to direct this water away from the building.	1
	v	Insulation over cold water pipes to avoid condensation on pipes in basements and crawlspaces.	2
	w	Zero urea formaldehyde interior panel products or seal with water-based sealer.	2
	x	No petroleum-based flooring materials in house.	3
	y	Low VOC adhesives for sheet goods	1

Vermont Building Green Scorecard (continued)

z	No carpet in house.		3
aa	If Carpet is installed, must meet CRI low emission label standard.		1
bb	Carpet with no site-applied adhesives.		1
	Design and build foundations to minimize soil gas entry:		
cc	Pipe all floor drains separate from footing drains; glue all floor drain joints.		1
dd	Provide above-grade cleanout of footing drains at high point of footing drains.		1
ee	Provide sub-slab 4" minimum crushed stone , connect sub slab drainage to footing drain.		1
ff	Provide exhaust fan in attached garage automatically controlled to run for pre-set period of time when garage door closes.		1
gg	Provide storage space sealed and isolated from the living space for toxic materials such as paint, gasoline cans, etc.		1
hh	Plumb/wire for central vacuum system.		1
ii	Central vacuum system.		3
kk	Non-chemical termite/carpenter ant barriers.		1
ll	Other non-chemical pest species resistant features.		1
mm	No paper faced gypsum under tiles in tubs, showers and spas.		2
nn	Built-in track-off mats or grates plus hard surface entry.		2
oo	Rough-in for sub-slab radon exhaust stack, 4" sub-slab crushed stone installed .		2
pp	Radon test after house is completed.		1
qq	Complete radon-exhaust system installed , if radon test is positive for radon.		2
rr	Heat detector (to automatically shut off heating system if fire).		1
ss	Non-radioactive smoke detector (per device).		1
tt	Low formaldehyde and low VOC-emission (250 grams per liter or less), including paints, solvents and adhesives.		3
uu	Install approach that meets the goal of this strategy not listed above (upon documentation and submission to VBG Program Committee).		TBD
2)	**Provide ventilation to remove pollutants generated in the house**		
a	Install filtered exhaust ventilation in kitchen.		Required
b	Install an automatic, effective ventilation system which is quiet (less than 1.5 sones for surface-mounted equipment) and has low energy consumption (less than .5 watts/cfm for bath fan EOV systems), providing at least 15 cfm per bedroom plus 15 cfm, such as one of the following:		Required
	i	Low-energy-use, quiet, durable bath fans with automatic control. As a minimum, the house must have an exhaust-only ventilation – EOV system or the following:	
	ii	Outside air ducted into furnace system return from outside, with fan-cycler control in conjunction with EOV system (points - see below)	
	iii	Ducted heat recovery ventilation system (points – see below).	
	iv	Non-fan-powered ventilation system, if proven effective through performance testing.	
c	Insulate all ventilation exchanging exhaust ductwork (minimum R-8) outside of the insulated envelope.		Required
d	Use rigid duct or other methods to keep fan back-pressure below 0.2" for EOV systems.		Required
e	Air seal ventilation ductwork.		Required
f	Exhaust fan or duct to central system in every bathroom that has a shower, spa or bathtub.		Required
g	Install furnace fan cycler control and automated damper fresh air inlet on return side of the distribution system with EOV system for forced-air houses with ECM air handler.		2
h	Install automatically controlled balanced heat recovery ventilation system with fresh air ducted to all occupied living spaces, and exhausted from all bathrooms and other moisture producing rooms. Recovery efficiency minimum 75%.		3
i	Central air or ventilation system with minimum 30% dust spot efficiency filters.		2
j	Post-construction testing to meet minimum air flow requirements or IAQ performance standards (submit results).		2
k	Install all ventilation exchanging exhaust ductwork inside of the insulated envelope.		2
l	Install approach that meets the goal of this strategy not listed above (upon documentation and submission to VBG Program Committee).		TBD
7. KEEPING IT GREEN -- OCCUPANT EDUCATION AND O&M			
1)	**Provide education for owners/occupants in the use and care of their dwellings**		
a	Educate occupants about the buildings' goals and strategies and impacts on costs of operating the building, while addressing obstacles to occupant education, such as language, literacy or elderly. Provide training of owners/occupants for all control systems in the house		Required

Vermont Building Green Scorecard (continued)

b	Provide a "User's Manual" for the house, including written operation instructions for the house, maintenance schedule, maintenance instructions, equipment literature, equipment warranties	Required
c	Provide "VBG Scorecard" to owners/occupants.	Required
d	Provide wire and valve labeling, diagrams and descriptions of system controls adequate for future maintenance and repair by a professional.	2
e	Provide photo record of framing with wiring and utilities installed, photos taken prior to installing insulation and interior sheathing/drywall. Photos keyed to location in or around home.	3
f	Label occupant controls for ease of use.	2
g	In rental housing provide user manual for new occupants.	1
h	Install approach that meets the goal of this strategy not listed above (upon documentation and submission to VBG Program Committee).	TBD

TOTAL POINTS ACHIEVED (points awarded for Approaches incorporated into home beyond Requirements)	
POINTS AWARDED FOR HOUSE SIZE (see House Size chart)	
VERMONT BUILT GREEN TOTAL POINTS (Total Points Achieved + Points Awarded for House Size)	

Vermont Building Green Scorecard (continued)

Vermont Built Green
House Size Points (version 6) for Scorecard v. 3.1 (4/2/03)

			Average or Smaller Home					Size Points	Min. Need
	Bedrooms								
	1	2	3	4	5	6			
Gross Square Footage of Home*	1700	2000	2300	2600	2900	3200		0	100
	1615	1900	2185	2470	2755	3040		3	97
	1530	1800	2070	2340	2610	2880		7	93
	1445	1700	1955	2210	2465	2720		12	88
	1360	1600	1840	2080	2320	2560		18	82
	1275	1500	1725	1950	2175	2400		25	75
	1190	1400	1610	1820	2030	2240		34	66
	1105	1300	1495	1690	1885	2080		45	55
	1020	1200	1380	1560	1740	1920		60	40
	935	1100	1265	1430	1595	1760		78	22
	850	1000	1150	1300	1450	1600		100	0
	765	900	1035	1170	1305	1440		127	0
	680	800	920	1040	1160			160	0
	595	700	805					199	0
	510	600						245	0
	425							300	0

			Average or Larger Home					Size Points	
	Bedrooms								
	1	2	3	4	5	6			
Gross Square Footage of Home*	1700	2000	2300	2600	2900	3200		0	100
	1870	2200	2530	2860	3190	3520		-6	106
	2040	2400	2760	3120	3480	3840		-13	113
	2210	2600	2990	3380	3770	4160		-20	120
	2380	2800	3220	3640	4060	4480		-28	128
	2550	3000	3450	3900	4350	4800		-38	138
	2720	3200	3680	4160	4640	5120		-48	148
	2890	3400	3910	4420	4930	5440		-59	159
	3060	3600	4140	4680	5220	5760		-70	170
	3230	3800	4370	4940	5510	6080		-84	184
	3400	4000	4600	5200	5800	6400		-100	200

(Right-side vertical label: Additional Points Needed for VBG Eligibility)

Houses above this size must develop a VBG "Big Green" Strategy with the VBG Review Committee

VBG House Size Score Directions:

After verifying compliance with VBG requirements, round your home's FT2 UP to the next FT2 on the chart, under your # of bedrooms. Read across to find your points

> Average Size Homes: Homes twice average size score zero.
< Average Size Homes: homes half the average size score the VBG threshold. The size points change progressively as the home size differs from average.

* Gross FT2 does not include *home business* or *unconditioned* space.
                                   (see definitions)